RECIPE CLIPPINGS

RECIPE JOURNAL

MURDOCH
BOOKS

Soups 4

Pasta 22

Rice & noodles 42

Seafood 62

Poultry 80

Meat 96

Salads & vegetables 116

Desserts 136

Baking 152

Jams & preserves 172

CONTENTS

SOUPS

SOUPS

The basis of a really flavoursome soup is a good-quality stock, and the best way to achieve that is to make your own.

MAKING STOCK

Stock should be cooked at simmering point rather than a full boil in order to extract maximum flavour and fragrance from the ingredients and prevent them disintegrating and forming unnecessary scum. Remove the fat before making the soup. To do this, strain, cool and refrigerate the stock. The solidified fat on top can then be spooned off. If you are using the stock immediately, a quick way is to strain the stock while it is still hot, then pass a double thickness of paper towels through it to absorb any fat. To stop your stocks from becoming cloudy they should not be boiled or stirred during cooking. All the stocks below will keep in the fridge for 2 days.

Chicken stock

Place 2 kg chicken bones or a whole boiling chicken in a large stockpot with 2 chopped carrots, 1 chopped leek, 1 chopped onion, 1 chopped celery stick, 1 bay leaf, a few parsley stalks (the leaves make it cloudy), a sprig of thyme and 6 litres of cold water. Bring to the boil, skim off any scum, then reduce the heat and simmer for 2 hours, skimming as necessary. Strain and refrigerate overnight. Makes about 3.5 litres.

Beef or veal stock

Preheat the oven to 220°C (425°F/Gas 7). Place 2 kg cut beef bones on an oven tray and roast for 20 minutes. Add 1 quartered onion, 1 chopped carrot, 1 chopped leek and 1 chopped celery stick and roast for 20 minutes more. Transfer the bones and vegetables to a large saucepan or stockpot, discarding any fat left on the roasting tray. Add 2 tablespoons tomato paste, a few parsley stalks, 1 bay leaf and 6 litres cold water. Bring to the boil, skimming any scum from the surface. Reduce the heat and simmer gently for 3–4 hours, skimming regularly. Strain and refrigerate. Makes about 3 litres.

Vegetable stock

Chop 1 onion, 4 carrots, 2 parsnips, 4 celery sticks and 2 leeks. Heat 1 tablespoon oil in a heavy-based saucepan or stockpot, add the vegetables and toss to coat in the oil. Cover and cook over medium heat for 5 minutes, without browning. Add 3 litres water and bring to the boil. Skim the surface, then add 2 bay leaves, 4 unpeeled garlic cloves and a few parsley stalks. Reduce the heat to low and simmer for 1 hour. Strain and refrigerate. Makes 2.5 litres.

Fish stock

Place 2 kg chopped and washed white fish bones (such as snapper, cod or whiting), including the heads and tails, into a large heavy-based saucepan. Add 1 diced celery stick, 1 diced onion, 1 diced unpeeled carrot, 1 diced leek and 2 litres water, and slowly bring to the boil. When boiling, skim the surface then add a sprig of fresh thyme and a bouquet garni. Reduce the heat and simmer gently for 20 minutes, frequently skimming the surface. Fish stock does not improve on additional cooking, in fact this can ruin it by making it bitter and cloudy. Ladle the stock in batches into a sieve lined with damp muslin sitting over a large bowl. To keep the stock clear don't press the solids through the sieve, simply leave the liquid to drain through undisturbed. Cool, then store in the fridge until needed. Makes about 1.5 litres.

FREEZING STOCK

Stock freezes well and will keep for 1–3 months. It's a good idea to freeze it in convenient, measurable portions. To freeze in 1 cup portions, for example, place a plastic bag in a measuring cup and fill with cooled stock. Extract the air from the bag and tightly seal. Once frozen, remove the bag from the cup, and label and date it. Another idea is to fill ice-cube trays with reduced stock, freeze and then store cubes in a freezer bag and use a few at a time to boost the flavour of sauces.

It is important not to season stocks and soups too early, as long cooking or storage concentrates the flavours. Peppercorns added too early can also make a stock cloudy and bitter. It is better to leave seasoning until you are nearly ready to serve.

CHICKEN AND VEGETABLE SOUP

3.5 litres chicken stock (see recipe on facing page)
1 large potato, cut into 2 cm cubes
2 carrots, sliced into rounds
1 large leek, sliced
200 g green beans
100 g yellow beans
150 g shelled peas
pinch of cayenne pepper
3 tablespoons chopped parsley

Follow the recipe on the facing page to make the chicken stock (make sure you use a whole boiling fowl as you will need the chicken flesh for the soup).

Remove the chicken pieces, cover and refrigerate until needed. Allow the stock to cool, then pour it through a strainer into a large pot, pressing the vegetables down firmly to get as much flavour as possible from them before discarding. Cover and refrigerate overnight.

The next day, spoon off the fat from the surface of the stock, then bring to the boil. Add the potato, carrot and leek and simmer for 30 minutes, or until tender. Trim the green and yellow beans and cut into 2 cm lengths. Add the peas and beans to the pan and simmer for a further 15 minutes.

Meanwhile, discard the chicken skin and remove the flesh from the bones. Cut the flesh into large cubes and add to the soup. Add the cayenne pepper and season well with salt and freshly ground black pepper. Simmer for 10 minutes, or until the chicken is warmed through. Stir in the parsley just before serving. Serves 4–6.

Note: This recipe is based on a white stock, which has quite a delicate flavour. If you prefer a more robust soup, start with a brown stock. To do this, simply brown the chicken pieces in vegetable oil for about 10 minutes, then brown the vegetables for 6–8 minutes. Add them both to the stockpot and continue with the recipe for white stock.

SOUP TIPS

Home-made bouquet garni

For a fresh, home-made bouquet garni with lots of flavour, simply tie herbs such as bay leaf, parsley and thyme stalks together with kitchen string. Alternatively, place the herbs inside the rib of leek greens then tie to secure with string.

Extra corn flavour

If making a fresh corn soup try boiling the cobs (after the corn kernels have been cut off) with the other vegetables to make the stock. It will enhance the soup to give that extra corn flavour.

Garnish ideas

Dressing up soups for special occasions is easy. Try deep-frying herbs or cutting julienne strips of leek to sit on top as a garnish. Char-grilled scallops arranged on top of a thick soup adds something special. Tortillas cut into strips and deep-fried or toasted in the oven work well with Mexican-style soups. A good-quality olive oil drizzled over hearty soups such as minestrone, puréed bean or legume soups not only tastes delicious but adds a lovely yet simple garnish.

Croutons

Croutons are easy to make and are a great garnish for soups. Remove the crusts from day-old bread and cut into cubes. Heat some oil in a frying pan, add the bread and whole garlic cloves if you like, and toss until evenly browned. Drain well on paper towels. Croutons can be stored in an airtight container to use as you need them. If they go soft, place on an oven tray and dry out in a moderate oven for 5 minutes.

Extra flavour in stocks

Add small amounts of lemon grass, kaffir lime leaves and ginger to your stock for an Asian influence, or try chopped tomatoes, saffron, garlic and lemon zest for a Mediterranean feel.

Vegetables in stock soups

If you are cooking a simple stock-based soup, such as chicken and vegetable soup, the cooking vegetables should be discarded before serving as their flavour and texture will have largely disappeared. Finely chop suitable fresh vegetables, add to the strained stock and cook for 20 minutes, or until tender.

SOUP

MINESTRONE

2 cups (400 g) dried cannellini or borlotti beans
1 tablespoon olive oil
100 g mild pancetta, finely diced
1 onion, chopped
1 carrot, diced
2 sticks celery, diced
1 large potato, diced
2 cloves garlic, crushed
3 tablespoons tomato paste (purée)
2 x 425 g cans crushed tomatoes
3 cups (750 ml) beef stock
1 cup (155 g) elbow macaroni or ditalini
75 g shredded cabbage
2 tablespoons shredded basil
shaved Parmesan, to serve
extra virgin olive oil, to serve

Put the beans in a large bowl, cover with cold water and leave to soak overnight.

Heat the oil in a large saucepan, add the pancetta and cook over medium heat, stirring, for 1–2 minutes, or until slightly crisp. Add the onion, carrot, celery, potato and garlic and cook for 1–2 minutes. Add the tomato paste, tomato, beef stock and drained beans. Bring to the boil, then reduce the heat and simmer, covered, for 40 minutes or until the beans are tender. (Do not add salt prior to this stage as it will toughen the beans.)

Add the pasta and cabbage and cook for 15 minutes. Season with salt and black pepper. Serve in deep bowls with the basil, shaved Parmesan, a drizzle of extra virgin olive oil and wood-fired bread. Serves 6.

PEA AND HAM SOUP

2¼ cups (500 g) yellow or green split peas
1½ tablespoons olive oil
2 onions, chopped
1 carrot, diced
3 sticks celery, finely chopped
1 kg ham bones or a smoked hock, chopped
1 bay leaf
2 sprigs of thyme
lemon juice, to taste (optional)

Soak the split peas in a large bowl of cold water for 6 hours. Drain well. Heat the oil in a large saucepan, add the onion, carrot and celery, and cook over low heat for 6–7 minutes, or until vegetables are soft but not brown.

Add the split peas, ham bones, bay leaf, thyme and 2.5 litres cold water, and bring to the boil. Reduce the heat and simmer, stirring occasionally, for 2 hours, or until the peas are tender. Discard the bay leaf and the sprigs of thyme.

Remove the ham bones from the soup and cool slightly. Remove the meat from the bone, discard the bones and chop the meat. Return the ham to the soup and reheat. Season to taste with freshly ground pepper and lemon juice. For a finer texture, the soup can be cooled and processed before returning the meat to the pan. Serves 6.

Classics SOUP

SOUP TIPS

Fish stock

The best fish bones for making a general fish stock are those from white-fleshed fish like cod or snapper. Avoid oily fleshed fish like salmon, tuna and mackerel as they create an overly fishy, oily stock which may be too strong to use as the base for other recipes.

Blending tips

If your soup requires blending, cool slightly before blending in batches. If there is too much soup in the blender it will spill over. If the soup is too hot, heat from the soup causes steam to push up which can lift the lid and cause not only a mess but nasty burns as well. If you have one, use a hand-held blender to blend the soup in one batch in the saucepan that it is cooked in. When making puréed vegetable soups the vegetables should only be cooked for the amount of time it takes for them to become tender, retaining some firmness, otherwise they become mushy and make the purée watery. Avoid using too many ingredients, particularly in puréed soups, as their flavours will cancel each other out and the soup will not taste of any component in particular.

Comforting chicken soup

Science has proven what generations of mothers have known for centuries: eat chicken soup when you have a cold. Chicken stock has a component which acts as an antibacterial agent, and also helps to clear blocked nasal passages.

Creamy soups

To enrich puréed soups, stir in thick cream, crème fraîche or sour cream as their high fat content keeps them stable when heated. Yoghurt can be added but take care not to boil as it curdles easily. A little of the hot soup should be mixed into the cream or yoghurt before stirring into the soup. Don't boil creamy soups as this can cause them to separate and appear curdled.

Bulk up clear soups

To add substance and interest to clear soups try stuffed pasta such as small ravioli or tortellini, soup pasta like orzo or stellini, shredded cooked chicken, small cooked prawns or thinly sliced mushrooms.

Pasta

PASTA

Pasta makes a simple yet satisfying meal. A few basic tips about cooking, draining and storing fresh and dried pasta will really help you make the most of this popular staple.

There is an almost endless choice of pasta shapes, sizes and sauces. On top of this, you can choose a dried, fresh or filled pasta to best suit your sauce. A quick, easy and economical meal, pasta can either be served as a first course as it is in Italy, or as a meal in its own right, accompanied by a simple salad and crusty bread.

ALL IN THE TIMING

Timing can make all the difference between a good pasta meal and a great one. Once cooked, pasta will not sit for long at all so it is important to have the sauce ready to go. While this is easy when serving slow-cooked dishes like spaghetti bolognaise, quick pasta sauces such as carbonara or alfredo should be prepared while the pasta cooks. Fresh pasta continues to cook if left to sit around so it is important to time the cooking of both carefully.

COOKING PASTA

- Pasta should be cooked in a large saucepan to allow room for expansion and to prevent sticking.

- Even if you need to cook large amounts of pasta don't cook more than 1 kg in the same saucepan at one time. Most kitchens are unlikely to have a pan large enough to cope with more than 1 kg.
- As a general rule, cook 500 g pasta in 4 litres of boiling water.
- Always bring the water to the boil before adding the pasta.
- Unsalted water will come to the boil faster than salted, so if you wish to add salt do it once the water is boiling.

IS IT COOKED?

Cooking times vary depending on the type of pasta. Fresh pasta, for instance, only takes a few minutes to cook, but dried pasta can take anything from 8 to 20 minutes, depending on the shape, quantity and brand. It's best to follow the packet instructions.

When you think the pasta is ready, the best test is to taste it. It should be just tender, not at all raw or soft and gluggy. This is referred to as *al dente*, which literally means 'to the tooth' in Italian.

AFTER IT'S COOKED

- Cooked pasta should not be over-drained as it needs to be a little wet for the sauce to coat it well.
- Some recipes reserve a little cooking water to add to the finished dish to stop it being too dry.
- If you have to leave cooked and drained pasta in the colander even for a few minutes, a little olive oil or butter tossed through hot pasta will help stop it sticking together.

MATCHING PASTA SHAPES AND SAUCES

There is no hard and fast rule as to which pasta shape to have with what sauce but traditionally a chunky pasta goes with a chunky sauce. This enables you to pick up the sauce with the pasta. Thin pastas are best with thin sauces. Smooth slender spaghetti will not hold a chunky sauce but will suit a sauce of olive oil or a fresh tomato-based sauce as this allows the strands to stay slippery and separate.

STORING PASTA

- Keep dried pasta stored in an airtight container in a cool dark place for up to 6 months. Dried whole wheat pasta will only last for 1 month or so.
- Fresh pasta must be refrigerated and will only keep for a couple of days so buy it as you need it.
- To freeze fresh pasta, wrap it in plastic, layering with greaseproof paper if necessary, and store in an airtight container for 4 months. Put the frozen pasta straight into boiling water when required.
- If your fresh pasta has a creamy filling it's best not to freeze it. The filling may become a little runny and the pasta could split during cooking.

SPAGHETTI BOLOGNAISE

2 tablespoons olive oil
2 cloves garlic, crushed
1 large onion, chopped
1 carrot, chopped
1 celery stick, chopped
50 g pancetta, finely chopped
500 g beef mince
2 cups (500 ml) beef stock
1$1/2$ cups (375 ml) red wine
2 x 425 g cans crushed tomatoes
2 tablespoons tomato paste (purée)
1 teaspoon sugar
2 tablespoons chopped parsley
500 g spaghetti or tagliatelle
freshly grated Parmesan, to serve

Heat the oil in a large deep saucepan. Add the garlic, onion, carrot, celery and pancetta, and cook, stirring, over low heat for 5 minutes, or until golden.

Increase the heat to medium and add the mince, breaking up any lumps with the back of a spoon as it cooks. Stir until well browned. Add the stock, red wine, crushed tomatoes, tomato paste, sugar and parsley. Bring to the boil, then reduce the heat and simmer, covered, for 1$1/2$ hours, stirring occasionally. Remove the lid and simmer for a further 1 hour, stirring occasionally. Season to taste with salt and freshly ground black pepper.

Cook the pasta according to the packet instructions until *al dente*. Drain well. Spoon the sauce over the pasta and serve sprinkled with Parmesan. Serves 4–6.

FRESH EGG PASTA

200g fine Semolina Flour

300g Plain Flour

5 eggs

Pinch Salt

Drizzle some Olive oil & work through to a stiff dough. Rest in fridge for 1hr. Then work it through the machine. Fold it, go down a no. & continue to put it through machine then pasta shredder or roll & cut by hand. Hang pasta on a curtain rod & let it dry for 10 mins before boiling.

PASTA TIPS

Choosing dried pasta

Pasta varies in quality, so try to choose a good Italian pasta as you will find the sauce tends to hold onto it better. Good-quality pastas are readily available in delicatessens or fine food stores and are often made by hand rather than machine. This makes a difference as hand-made dried pasta is more unevenly textured than smooth machine-made types, so they hold sauces more effectively. They are a little more expensive than supermarket brands but worth it for the extra flavour and texture.

Swapping pasta shapes

If substituting one pasta for another, choose a pasta of a similar shape and size to avoid having too much or not enough sauce.

Non-stick pasta

Adding a tablespoon of oil to the pasta when cooking can help prevent pasta sticking and some people like to cook it in salted water to enhance the flavour.

Distributing the sauce evenly

It is traditional to toss the cooked pasta with most sauces as this allows the sauce to coat the pasta in every crevice and every strand, which means all those eating it have an evenly sauced serving. There are some exceptions, such as spaghetti bolognaise and duck ragout, which are served with the sauce spooned over the pasta.

Tomato-based sauces

If tomatoes are not in season it is often better to use canned whole Italian tomatoes for a good robust flavour. Another idea is to try roasting or semi-drying tomatoes in the oven before making the sauce, as this intensifies their flavour.

Pasta with wilted greens

When adding green leaves such as baby spinach or rocket (arugula) to a pasta dish, stir them in at the end and they will wilt into the dish without further cooking.

Seafood without cheese

Traditionally, Italians do not serve seafood-based pastas with any cheese. This is so the delicate flavour of the seafood is not overpowered.

PASTA

PASTA PRIMAVERA

120 g broad beans, fresh or frozen
150 g asparagus, cut into short lengths
350 g fresh tagliatelle
100 g French beans, cut into short lengths
120 g peas, fresh or frozen
30 g butter
1 small fennel bulb, thinly sliced
1½ cups (375 ml) double (thick) cream
2 tablespoons grated Parmesan, plus extra to serve

Bring a large saucepan of water to the boil. Add 1 teaspoon of salt, the broad beans and the asparagus and simmer for 3 minutes.

Remove the vegetables with a slotted spoon and set aside. Add the tagliatelle to the saucepan and, when it has softened, stir in the French beans and the peas (if you're using frozen peas add them a few minutes later). Cook for about 4 minutes, or until the pasta is *al dente*.

Meanwhile, heat the butter in a large frying pan. Add the fennel and cook over moderately low heat, without colouring, for 5 minutes. Add the cream, season with salt and pepper and cook at a low simmer.

Peel the skins from the broad beans. Drain the pasta, French beans and peas and add to the frying pan. Add 2 tablespoons of Parmesan and the broad beans and asparagus. Toss lightly to coat. Serve immediately, with extra Parmesan. Serves 4.

SPAGHETTI ALLA PUTTANESCA

4 tablespoons olive oil
1 small onion, finely chopped
2 garlic cloves, finely sliced
1 small red chilli, cored, seeded and sliced
6 anchovy fillets, finely chopped
400 g tin chopped tomatoes
1 tablespoon finely chopped oregano or
¼ teaspoon dried oregano
⅔ cup (100 g) pitted black olives, halved
1 tablespoon capers, chopped if large
400 g spaghetti

Heat the olive oil in a large saucepan and add the onion, garlic and chilli. Fry gently for 6 minutes, or until the onion is soft. Add the anchovies and cook, stirring, until well mixed.

Add the tomatoes, oregano, olives and capers and bring to the boil. Reduce the heat, season and leave to simmer.

Meanwhile, cook the pasta in a large saucepan of boiling salted water until *al dente*. Drain, toss well with the sauce and serve at once. Serves 4.

Classic PASTA

PASTA
SERVING IDEAS

Pasta with rocket (arugula) and Parmesan
For a quick and delicious pasta meal, toss fettucine with some roughly chopped rocket leaves and rocket pesto, top with shaved Parmesan and drizzle with good-quality olive oil.

Traditional favourite
One of southern Italy's most common dishes is a simple bowl of pasta aglio e olio. Just-cooked pasta is coated with a dressing of crushed garlic, extra virgin olive oil and finely chopped fresh flat-leaf parsley. Try adding some fresh chilli for extra bite.

Capers
For an extra burst of flavour, deep-fry capers until crispy and sprinkle over pasta with shellfish sauces.

Breadcrumb topping
Toasted or fried flavoured breadcrumbs make a quick pasta topping called pangritata. Heat ½ cup (125 ml) good-quality olive oil in a heavy-based frying pan over low to medium heat. Add 1 crushed garlic clove, a tablespoon of finely chopped fresh herbs (such as thyme or basil) and 200 g fresh breadcrumbs and stir until crisp and golden. Drain on paper towels and season to taste with salt and pepper.

Pine nuts
Toasting pine nuts or other nuts before using in pesto or tossing through pasta will enhance their flavour.

Burnt butter and sage sauce
Filled pasta such as ravioli or tortellini can be served with a simple sauce of brown butter, sage and pepper. To brown the butter, heat it in a frying pan until it melts and just starts to turn brown.

Revive a simple tomato sauce
Ready-made tomato passata is wonderfully versatile and can be used as the basis for many pasta sauces, such as bolognaise, napolitana or marinara. The addition of chilli turns it into an arrabiata sauce, while crisp bacon or prosciutto makes it an amatriciana sauce. For those who prefer a strongly flavoured sauce, anchovies, black olives and capers transform it into a hearty puttanesca sauce.

MAKING
FRESH PASTA

Before you start

If possible, use plain bread flour for making pasta, though a mixture of half semolina flour and half bread flour also works well. Don't be tempted to rush through the kneading stage as it works the flour's gluten content, resulting in a firm yet tender dough. This is especially important if you are making the dough by hand, as the more elastic the dough is the easier it will be to roll out. Rolling is equally important as it makes the pasta more porous, enabling it to absorb a maximum amount of its accompanying sauce, while the thinness ensures that it stays tender after cooking.

Flavouring and colourings such as fresh herbs, spices such as saffron, and vegetable purées like beetroot or spinach can be added when making fresh pasta at the stage of mixing the flour with the wet ingredients.

Basic plain dough recipe

To make enough pasta dough to serve 6 people as a first course or 4 as a main course, you will need 300 g bread or plain flour, 3 large eggs, 30 ml olive oil (optional) and a good pinch of salt. Mound the flour on a work surface or in a large ceramic bowl, and make a well in the centre. Break the eggs into the well and add the oil and salt. Using a fork, begin to whisk the eggs and oil together, incorporating a little flour as you go. Gradually blend the flour with the eggs, working from the centre out. Use your free hand to hold the mound in place and stop leakage if any egg escapes.

Knead the dough on a lightly floured surface for about 6 minutes, or until you have a soft, smooth elastic dough which is dry to the touch. Use smooth, light strokes, turning the dough as you fold and press. If it is sticky, knead in a little flour. Cover the dough with a tea towel and allow to rest for 30 minutes.

Using a pasta machine or rolling pin, roll out the dough thinly and cut into sheets or thin strips. When making your own pasta sheets, make extra, blanch and then wrap well and freeze in an airtight container. They can be thawed later to be used in lasagne, or filled and baked for cannelloni.

RICE
& NOODLES

RICE & NOODLES

Rice and noodles are excellent store cupboard staples. Cooked correctly, they can be served as an accompaniment or, as in the case of risotto, form the basis of a delicious main meal.

COOKING RICE

Whether you need to rinse rice before cooking depends on the type of rice you are using and the dish being prepared. Rinsing rice removes any powdered starch clinging to the grains, or if rice is sold in sacks it can have dust and stones mixed in which obviously need to be rinsed off. These days, most packaged rices don't require washing (unless the recipe specifies it) as they have already been carefully processed before packaging. Some short-grain rices are rinsed before cooking to separate the grains rather than allowing them to stick. The reverse is true for arborio rice which is used for risotto, as the characteristic creamy risotto texture is achieved by slowly releasing the rice's starch content.

Rice just about trebles in size when cooked, so 1 cup raw white rice makes about 3 cups cooked rice. Brown rice makes a little less, with 1 cup raw rice making about 2 cups cooked rice.

There are two methods of cooking rice — the absorption method and the fast-boiling method.

Absorption method

Put the rice in a saucepan and rest a fingertip lightly on the surface, adding water until it comes up to the first finger joint. Bring to the boil for 1 minute, then cover, reduce the heat to as low as possible and cook for 10 minutes, or until all the water is absorbed into the rice and dimples form on the surface. Remove from the heat and leave, covered, for 10 minutes to finish steaming through. Fluff gently with a fork before serving.

Fast-boiling method

Bring a large saucepan of water to a fast boil. Pour in the rice and cook for 12 minutes, stirring occasionally (brown rice takes about 40 minutes). Drain well.

CHOOSING THE RIGHT NOODLES

It is a good idea to match the noodle with the sauce, topping or soup. When in doubt, a general guide is to use noodles from the same cuisine as the dish you wish to make. For example, use Japanese noodles such as soba, udon and ramen with Japanese dishes, and Chinese noodles such as egg or wheat noodles in Chinese dishes. Fresh or dried wheat noodles are a good all-purpose noodle to have as a stand-by. As a general rule, dried noodles can be kept in a cool, dark place for months (check the use-by date).

COOKING NOODLES

- It's very difficult to undercook a noodle but very easy to overcook one, so when boiling or soaking your noodles make sure that they are *al dente* (firm to the bite). This stops them breaking up when they are added to a soup or stir-fry. If adding noodles to soup, cook them separately, transfer to serving bowls, then ladle on the soup.

- Like pasta, Japanese noodles need to be cooked in plenty of boiling water in a large saucepan. Dried soba noodles (also known as buckwheat noodles) require very little cooking time before using. Do not overcook or they will break up and look messy in your dish.

- Try soaking fresh noodles such as Hokkien briefly in boiling water before cooking with them. This will not only help separate them but they plump up and become quite tender. They are also easier to toss through a stir-fry.

- Dried noodles such as rice vermicelli, egg noodles and wheat noodles can also be placed in a heatproof bowl, covered with boiling water and soaked for a few minutes until softened, before they are used in a stir-fry or to make a noodle salad. If they are to be used in soup they can be cooked direct from the packet in the soup stock a few minutes before serving.

RISOTTO MILANESE

15 saffron threads
1.5 litres chicken stock
1 cup (250 ml) dry white wine
60 g butter
1 large onion, finely chopped
2 cups (440 g) arborio rice
100 g freshly grated Parmesan

Coarsely crush the saffron in a mortar and pestle or finely chop. Place in a bowl and add 1 tablespoon hot water. Leave for 10 minutes. Heat the stock and wine in a saucepan, cover and keep at a low simmer.

Melt the butter in a large saucepan over low heat. Add the onion and cook, stirring, for 5 minutes, or until soft. Stir in the rice until the grains are coated in the butter.

Add the saffron and its liquid and ½ cup (125 ml) hot stock, stirring over medium heat until the liquid is absorbed. Continue adding the stock, ½ cup (125 ml) at a time, stirring constantly, for 20 minutes, or until all the liquid is absorbed and the rice is tender and creamy. Add half the Parmesan and season to taste with salt and freshly ground pepper. Cover and leave for 5 minutes, then sprinkle with the remaining Parmesan and serve. Serves 4.

RICE COOKING TIPS

Paella tip

When making paella it is best not to stir right to the bottom, as the aim is to produce a prized thin, crisp layer at the bottom of the pan.

Cooking risotto

When making risotto, use a heavy-based saucepan as this allows the rice to cook more evenly. The saucepan should not be too wide as otherwise the liquid will evaporate too quickly, before having a chance to be absorbed by the rice. It is very important to stir continuously to obtain the creamy texture.

Asian sausages and rice

When cooking an Asian meal, dried Chinese lap cheong sausages can be placed directly on top of the rice in the saucepan or rice cooker, before cooking, as they will cook in the rice's steam and also infuse the rice with their flavour. To serve, remove from the top of the cooked rice and slice into diagonal pieces.

A splash of wine in risotto

If using wine in risotto it should always be heated with the stock, otherwise it can cause the rice to taste too 'winey' if added directly to the dish.

Use up last night's leftover rice

Leftover rice is perfect for making fried rice or stir-frying. The grains become easily separated when cold, enabling other ingredients to mix through easily. Always keep cooked rice in the refrigerator, never at room temperature, and re-use very quickly — cooked rice stored at an incorrect temperature can lead to food poisoning.

Making sushi

When making sushi, dip your hands in water to spread the rice out onto the nori to prevent the rice sticking to your hands.

Flavouring rice

Different flavourings can be added to rice to complement the dish you're serving it with. Try bruised lemon grass and shredded kaffir lime leaves for a Thai curry or for a richer flavour, rice can be cooked in a mixture of water and coconut milk.

RICE & NOODLES

NOODLES WITH BEEF

500 g unsliced fresh rice noodles
2 tablespoons peanut oil
2 eggs, lightly beaten
500 g rump steak, thinly sliced
3 tablespoons kecap manis
1¹/₂ tablespoons soy sauce
1¹/₂ tablespoons fish sauce
300 g Chinese broccoli, cut into 5 cm lengths
¹/₄ teaspoon white pepper
lemon wedges, to serve

Cut the noodles lengthways into 2 cm strips. Gently separate the strips—run under cold water if necessary. (Rice noodles should not be refrigerated, as they are very difficult to separate when cold.)

Heat a wok over medium heat, add 1 tablespoon oil and swirl to coat. Add the egg, swirl to coat and cook for 1–2 minutes, or until set. Remove and slice.

Reheat the wok over high heat, add the remaining oil and swirl to coat. Cook the beef in batches for 3 minutes, or until brown. Remove.

Reduce the heat to medium, add the noodles and cook for 2 minutes. Combine the kecap manis, soy and fish sauces. Add to the wok with the broccoli and white pepper, then stir-fry for 2 minutes. Return the egg and beef to the wok and cook for 3 minutes, or until the broccoli has wilted and the noodles are soft but not breaking. Serve with the lemon. Serves 4–6.

PRAWN PILAU

2 cups (400 g) basmati rice
60 g butter
1 onion, finely chopped
2 cloves garlic, finely chopped
1 cm x 4 cm piece fresh ginger, peeled and grated
1 fresh green chilli, finely chopped
3 teaspoons coriander seeds
1 teaspoon ground turmeric
2 cardamom pods, cracked
1 kg raw medium prawns, peeled and deveined,
with tails intact
¹/₂ cup (80 g) raw cashew nuts
¹/₃ cup (80 ml) lemon juice
¹/₂ cup (25 g) chopped coriander (cilantro) leaves

Rinse the rice under cold water until the water runs clear. Drain well. Melt 30 g butter over low heat in a large saucepan, then add the onion and cook for 3 minutes, or until soft. Add the garlic, ginger, chilli, coriander seeds and turmeric, and cook for 2 minutes.

Add the rice to the saucepan and cook for 1 minute, then add the cardamom pods and 1 litre water. Bring to the boil, then reduce the heat and simmer, covered, for 10 minutes, or until the rice is tender. Remove from the heat and leave, covered, for 5 minutes to steam.

Melt the remaining butter in a frying pan, add the prawns and cashew nuts and cook over high heat for 3–4 minutes, or until the prawns are pink and cooked through. Add both to the rice, then add the lemon juice and coriander and stir everything together. Season with salt and pepper, and serve. Serves 4–6.

RICE &
NOODLES

QUICK RICE RECIPES

Garlic rice

To make a simple garlic-flavoured rice, finely chop a clove or more of garlic, lightly fry in a small amount of oil or butter, then gently stir it through just-cooked rice. If you like, half a teaspoon of saffron or turmeric can also be added to the cooking water to delicately colour the rice and give it an aromatic flavour.

Simple pilaf

Cook the rice in chicken or fish stock instead of water for a more flavoursome result, then toss in butter or oil with spices to turn it into a simple pilaf side dish. To make this a heartier meal, simply stir in toasted nuts, some dried fruit and cooked meat or chicken.

Saffron rice

For saffron-infused rice to accompany Spanish dishes, soak a pinch of saffron strands in 2 tablespoons boiling water for 5 minutes, then squeeze the strands to extract all the colour and make the water golden. Discard the strands, reserving the liquid. Sprinkle the saffron water over the rice and cook following your usual method. To add Indian flavours to saffron rice, add 6 whole cloves, a cinnamon stick and 3 lightly bruised cardamom pods to the cooking water. Make sure you remove them before serving the rice.

Cheesy risotto snack

Leftover risotto can be mixed with some egg, rolled into balls with a cube of mozzarella pushed into the centre, then coated in breadcrumbs and deep-fried until crisp.

Middle Eastern rice

To add a hint of Middle Eastern spice to your rice, add ¼ teaspoon ground coriander or allspice to the cooking water. Alternatively, cook the rice as you would normally, then just before serving stir in finely chopped fresh dill, parsley or coriander (cilantro) leaves and a tablespoon of melted ghee or butter. For added texture, toasted pine nuts, shelled pistachios, flaked almonds or currants can also be stirred in before serving.

ALL ABOUT NOODLES

Making Mee Grob

When deep-frying dried rice vermicelli to make Mee Grob, break the noodles into smaller pieces so they puff up and fry evenly. This will avoid hard uncooked bits of noodle.

New Year's Eve in Japan

In Japan every New Year's Eve, as the bells strike midnight, everyone consumes a bowl of 'tashikoshi' soba ('passing of the year' soba). The long strands of soba represent long life for the coming year.

Polite to slurp as you eat!

When eating Japanese noodles the etiquette is to eat them in such a way that you have to suck in a little air to cool them down, resulting in a slurping sound. If there is no slurp it is assumed that you haven't enjoyed your noodles. Whether you choose to share this information with your children is entirely up to you!

Noodle shops

When cooking noodles in noodle shops they are cooked in huge batches and reheated as needed. The chef puts a portion of noodles into a deep bamboo colander and drops it into boiling water to reheat before serving. If you order soup in a noodle shop, they will compile it before your very eyes, starting with the noodles in the base of the bowl, then spooning the stock over the top. This keeps the meal fresh and reduces the risk of overcooking the noodles.

Chilled somen noodles

Somen noodles are very delicate and become soft and limp quickly, so care needs to be taken when cooking. They are quite commonly served chilled with ice cubes and eaten in the warmer months. Serve with a dipping sauce of dashi, Japanese soy sauce, mirin and wasabi (optional), and garnish with finely chopped spring onions (scallions).

Cutting translucent noodles

When cooking with fine translucent noodles that are packaged in bundles, such as bean thread vermicelli, use kitchen scissors to separate them before adding to the saucepan.

SEAFOOD

SEAFOOD

Seafood is divided into three main categories: fish, crustaceans and molluscs. To get the very best out of seafood it is important to match the type of seafood with the best cooking method.

COOKING SEAFOOD

Never overcook seafood or it will be dry, tough and rubbery. Remove it from the heat as soon as it is just done — the internal heat will finish the cooking process. Certain types of seafood, such as salmon, trout and oysters, can be eaten raw. If you are serving seafood raw, make sure it is very fresh and clean, otherwise it may be spoiled by harmful bacteria. Some seafood can also be eaten just rare to medium rare, such as the more meaty oily fish like tuna and swordfish, while delicate scallops only need to be seared on both sides to lightly cook through.

Steaming

This is suitable for nearly all types of fish (eg white-fleshed fillets, small whole fish) and shellfish (crabs and prawns), but it is best for seafood with delicate flesh. Bivalves such as mussels are cooked in a little wine or liquid in a tightly sealed pan over high heat. Other seafood should be cooked over simmering liquid (water, stock or wine), not in it. Fish should not overlap or be touching or it will not cook evenly.

Poaching

Gentle simmering of seafood in a liquid ensures it stays moist. The liquid should be kept so that it is not boiling, but is slightly moving on top. Whole fish, cutlets and fillets can be poached (use special fish poachers for large whole fish). Squid and shellfish such as lobster and clams are delicious poached.

Baking

Baking whole fish in a moderately hot oven is one of the simplest cooking methods. It's a good idea to put the fish on a vegetable that has a high water content to help the fish keep its moisture. Haddock, sea bass and snapper are particularly suited to this method.

Stewing and casseroling

Most fish are suitable for this, from delicate-fleshed fish such as John Dory to firm-fleshed bream, but do take care not to overcook it. Avoid strongly flavoured oily fish such as mackerel or herring as the flavour will overpower the other seafood. Mussels, prawns and lobster make a delicious addition to stews.

Grilling and barbecuing

The key to successful grilling or barbecuing is to preheat the hotplate. Cutlets or fish steaks from large oily fish (such as salmon or mackerel) or small whole fish (such as red mullet) are best suited, though any firm-fleshed fish can be used. The fish should be no more than 5 cm thick or it will overcook on the outside before cooking through.

Deep-frying

Battered or coated fish is cooked in very hot oil (nearly twice the temperature of boiling water), hence the need for a protective coating. Small whole fish such as whitebait, sardines and thin fillets and firm-fleshed shellfish are suitable for this method. Thicker larger fish and fillets tend to dry out and overcook on the outside before cooking through.

Pan-frying

Dust fish fillets with seasoned flour, then cook in a layer of hot oil or butter. The flour forms a golden crust and the fish stays moist and doesn't stick to the pan. This is suited to firm white-fleshed fish, skinned fillets of flat fish such as medium whole fish, fish cutlets and steaks. Cook thicker fillets over high heat until a golden crust forms on both sides, then reduce the heat so the centre cooks through.

Stir-frying

Seafood is cooked quickly in oil in a wok or large frying pan. Do this in batches so the temperature of the wok doesn't drop, thus stewing the food, then return all the food to the wok at the end to heat through. Firm-fleshed fish, prawns, squid and cuttlefish are well suited to stir-frying.

BAKED SALMON WITH DILL GREMOLATA

2 kg whole salmon, cleaned, gutted and scaled
2 spring onions (scallions), roughly chopped
3 sprigs of dill
1/2 lemon, thinly sliced
6 black peppercorns
1/4 cup (60 ml) dry white wine
3 bay leaves

GREMOLATA
1/2 cup (30 g) chopped dill
2 cloves garlic, finely chopped
1 tablespoon grated lemon rind

Preheat the oven to 180°C (350°F/Gas 4). Rinse the salmon under cold running water and pat dry inside and out with paper towels. Stuff the salmon cavity with spring onion, dill, lemon and peppercorns.

Brush a large double-layered piece of foil with oil and lay the salmon on the foil. Sprinkle on the wine and arrange the bay leaves over the top. Fold the foil over and wrap up, covering the salmon tightly. Place in a shallow baking dish and bake for 30 minutes. Turn off the heat and leave the salmon in the oven for 45 minutes with the door closed.

To make the gremolata, place the dill, garlic and lemon rind in a bowl and toss until combined. Set aside until ready to serve.

Remove the salmon from the oven, undo the foil and carefully peel away the skin on the top side. Gently flip the salmon onto a serving plate and remove the skin from the other side. Pull out the fins and any visible bones. Serve at room temperature with lemon slices and the gremolata. Serves 8.

Note: Some people like to remove the head from the fish before serving — this depends on the size of the serving dish and personal preference. This recipe is also delicious with ocean trout.

SEAFOOD TIPS

Stock basics
Don't throw away good-quality fish, crustacean or shellfish trimmings as these make great bases for stocks. Freeze until you have some time to make stock.

Peeling prawns
When peeling prawns for entertaining and you don't want your guests to arrive to a smelly kitchen, try wrapping up the shells and freezing them until the rubbish is due to be collected.

Storing seafood
When storing raw seafood in the fridge, place it on the bottom shelf as this will prevent juices dripping onto and contaminating other food.

Per person
An ideal main course serve of fish is 200 g per person. If choosing fillets, try to buy ones of a similar size and thickness so they will cook evenly and be ready at the same time.

Quick marinating
Seafood should not marinate for long as there is little connective tissue — 20 to 30 minutes is usually enough.

Sashimi
When cutting fish for sashimi always cut across the grain as this improves the texture of the sashimi. Only the best quality and freshest fish should be used.

Lemon juice does the trick
After handling raw seafood squeeze some lemon juice on your hands before washing to remove fishy odours.

Deveining prawns
Peeled prawns should be deveined before cooking. You may devein either by using your fingers or a small skewer to gently pull out the intestinal tract, or by making a small slit down the back of the prawn and scraping out the dark vein.

Court bouillon
A simple "court bouillon" is a liquid flavoured with wine, onion, carrot, celery and bouquet garni. This is used to poach seafood, and other aromatics such as lemon grass, ginger, lemon, lime or fennel may be added to enhance the flavour of the dish.

SEAFOOD

STEAMED FISH WITH GINGER

4 whole bream, snapper or flounder,
each about 350 g, scaled and cleaned
2 tablespoons julienned ginger
1/4 cup (60 ml) peanut oil
2–3 tablespoons soy sauce
6 spring onions (scallions), sliced diagonally
coriander (cilantro) sprigs, to garnish

Make 2 diagonal cuts in the thickest part of each fish on both sides, then put in a lined bamboo or other large steamer. Cover and steam for 10 minutes, or until cooked (the fish will flake easily when tested with a fork).

Place each whole fish on a serving plate and scatter some of the fresh julienned ginger over the fish. Heat the oil in a small saucepan over medium heat until the oil begins to smoke. Pour some hot oil over each fish. The oil will sizzle and splatter, so stand back a little (the oil must be very hot or the fish won't go crisp and may seem oily). Drizzle the soy sauce over the fish and garnish with spring onion and coriander.

This fish is delicious served with steamed rice and steamed or stir-fried Asian vegetables. Serves 4.

MUSSELS IN CHUNKY TOMATO SAUCE

1.5 kg black mussels
3 tablespoons olive oil
1 large onion, diced
4 cloves garlic, finely chopped
810 g can diced tomatoes
3 tablespoons tomato paste (purée)
1/4 cup (30 g) pitted black olives
1 tablespoon capers
1/2 cup (125 ml) fish stock
3 tablespoons chopped parsley

Scrub the mussels with a stiff brush and pull out the hairy beards. Discard any damaged mussels, or those that don't close when tapped on the bench.

In a large saucepan, heat the olive oil and cook the onion and garlic over medium heat for 1–2 minutes, until softened. Add the tomato, tomato paste, olives, capers, and fish stock. Bring to the boil, then reduce the heat and simmer, stirring occasionally, for 20 minutes, or until the sauce is thick.

Stir in the mussels and cover the saucepan. Shake or toss the mussels occasionally, and cook for 4–5 minutes, or until the mussels begin to open. Once they have all opened, remove the pan from the heat. Discard any unopened mussels.

Just before serving, toss the chopped parsley through. Serve with crusty bread. Serves 4–6.

Classics SEAFOOD

SEAFOOD TIPS

Not so smoky

If using smoked fish (eg haddock) or salted fish (eg cod), soak in cold water or milk for a few hours to lessen the smoked or salty taste.

'Velveting' prawns

Popular in Chinese cookery, the technique called 'velveting' will result in silky prawns which may then be cooked as the recipe dictates. For every kilo of peeled, deveined prawns, add ½ cup (60 g) of cornflour and 1 tablespoon of bicarbonate soda, and massage into the prawns for a couple of minutes. Rinse under cold running water, and massage under the water for a further 5 minutes. Drain and dry, then use according to the recipe.

Fragrant steamed fish

Steaming fish in a paper or foil packet with the addition of coriander, ginger and spring onions is a simple and delicate way of preparing most cuts of fish.

Hot oil to give a crisp skin

A lovely way to finish a steamed small whole fish is to lightly pour over a little smoking hot peanut or sesame oil just before serving to crisp the skin.

Stir in at the end

Add shellfish or chunks of fish to curries and soups at the end of cooking as they will not take long to cook through, then stir gently to prevent them breaking up.

Perfect scallops

When searing scallops make sure the pan is very hot to prevent the scallops releasing their juice and poaching in the liquid. Scallops will be dry if over-cooked, and are best cooked quickly to medium rare.

Cooking live shellfish

Place live shellfish in the freezer for 2 hours before preparing them. This puts them to sleep gently rather than having to skewer them to kill them.

Soak clams and pipis

When using clams or pipis, soak them in cold water for 2 hours prior to cooking, changing the water at regular intervals, as this will encourage them to release any sand trapped in the shell.

POULTRY

POULTRY

Poultry (particularly chicken) is a wonderfully versatile base ingredient that suits many different cooking styles.

CUTS OF CHICKEN

Chicken cuts include: double or single breast on the bone, with skin or without; breast fillets; tenderloins (the part just behind the breast); marylands (the whole thigh and leg); thigh cutlets; thigh fillets; wings; and drumsticks.

Chicken cuts and cooking methods

- **For roasting:** whole roasting chickens, chicken on the bone, baby chickens and whole breasts.
- **For grilling:** chicken halves and quarters, wings, drumsticks, marylands and thigh cutlets.
- **For barbecuing:** chicken halves, whole breasts, wings, drumsticks, marylands and thigh cutlets.
- **For stir-frying:** breast fillets, thigh fillets, livers and tenderloins.
- **For pan-frying:** chicken off the bone, tenderloins and mince.
- **For deep-frying:** drumsticks, wings, thigh fillets, and mince (as patties).
- **For casseroling/stewing:** chicken on the bone (wings, thighs, drumsticks) and whole chickens.
- **For poaching:** whole chickens, breast fillets, thighs.
- **For making stock:** bones, necks and giblets.

ROASTING POULTRY

Whichever cut of poultry you are cooking, make sure it is cooked thoroughly, especially when it is on the bone, as undercooked poultry harbours harmful bacteria that can lead to food poisoning.

As a guide, cook a whole chicken in the oven at 190°C (375°F/Gas 5) for 15–20 minutes per 500 g plus an extra 15–20 minutes. For a whole turkey, preheat the oven to 180°C (350°F/Gas 4) and cook for 20 minutes per 500 g for a bird under 4.5 kg, or for 16–18 minutes per 500 g for a bird over 4.5 kg. If you are roasting a bird with stuffing, allow an extra 20–25 minutes to the overall time.

Always test for doneness before serving, and leave in the oven until it is fully cooked. Keep in mind that when cooking poultry on the bone, the dark meat (legs and thighs) will take longer to cook than the white (breast).

Frequent basting when roasting a bird is the secret to well-browned crispy skin with juicy flesh. Butter flavoured with garlic, grated lemon zest or finely chopped fresh herbs can be rubbed between the skin and the meat to infuse it with aromatic flavours and help keep the breast meat lovely and moist. Flavours that complement chicken include lime, saffron, leek, wine, olive oil, olives, fennel, mushrooms, mustard and cream, and herbs and spices, such as rosemary, parsley, thyme, chilli, coriander and ginger.

When is it cooked?

To test whether roasted poultry is cooked, insert a skewer into the thickest part of the bird (the thigh). If it is cooked, the juices will run clear (not pink). You can also test by twisting or jiggling the leg. If it moves easily in its socket, the chicken is cooked. Pan-fried, grilled or barbecued chicken is cooked when the meat is tender enough to fall easily off the bone when tested with a fork. Test fillets for doneness by cutting into the thickest part: if the juices run clear and the flesh is not pink, it's cooked.

CARVING

- Allow the chicken to rest for at least 10 minutes in a warm place before carving (20 minutes for a turkey). This will make it slice more easily as the muscles relax, and will let the juices reabsorb throughout the bird, keeping the meat moist.
- Place on a carving board or secure surface. Using a two-pronged fork to hold the bird and a sharp knife, cut around the leg, taking in a reasonable amount of flesh from the sides, firstly cutting through the skin and then using the tip of the knife to separate the bone at the joint.
- Cut above the wing joint, through the breast bone. Separate the legs by cutting into the thigh and drumstick.
- Carve breast meat in slices parallel to the rib cage.

OVEN-ROASTED ROSEMARY CHICKEN

1 onion, chopped
1 celery stick, chopped
1 carrot, chopped
2 cups (500 ml) chicken stock
1.8 kg chicken
6 large sprigs of rosemary
6 cloves garlic
¼ cup (60 ml) olive oil
1 teaspoon sea salt flakes
1 tablespoon plain flour

Preheat the oven to 190°C (375°F/Gas 5). Place the onion, celery and carrot in the base of a roasting tin and pour in the chicken stock.

Wipe the chicken and pat dry with paper towels. Season the cavity well and place four rosemary sprigs and 4 cloves garlic inside. Chop the remaining rosemary and garlic and place in a bowl with 2 tablespoons oil, the sea salt flakes and freshly ground black pepper. Rub the mixture all over the chicken, then sit the chicken on top of the vegetables in the roasting tin. Cook for 1–1¼ hours, or until golden and tender, and the juices run clear when the thigh is pierced with a skewer.

Remove the chicken from the roasting tin, cover and leave for 15 minutes while you make the gravy. Discard the vegetables and strain the pan juices into a jug (skim any fat off the top). Heat the remaining oil in a small saucepan over medium heat, add the flour and stir for 1 minute. Gradually stir in the pan juices until you have a smooth gravy. Stir in any juices from the resting chicken, then reduce the heat to low while you carve the chicken. Serve with a selection of roast vegetables. Serves 4.

CHICKEN TIPS

Take out the wishbone

If you remove the wishbone before roasting a whole chicken, it will be much easier to carve the breast into thin slices. To do this, pull back the skin from the neck cavity and use your fingers to feel for the wishbone just inside. Cut around it with a sharp knife, then scrape the meat away. Cut the wishbone at the joint and lift it out.

Serves four

As a rough guide, 750 g–1 kg skinless, boneless chicken or 1.5–1.8 kg chicken pieces on the bone will serve four people.

Lower in fat

Some people prefer to eat chicken without the skin. This eliminates much of the fat from the chicken as the fat lies in a layer just underneath the skin.

Chicken livers

When using chicken livers, remove any green tinges as even the smallest amount imparts a bitter flavour.

Stuffing adds moisture

As well as imparting extra flavour and expanding a meal, stuffing a whole chicken helps to retain moistness in the breast meat. When cooking a stuffed chicken increase the cooking time by about 25 minutes.

Chicken kebabs

When making chicken kebabs it is better to use thigh rather than breast fillets as they have more moisture, and do not dry out as quickly over the high, dry heat.

Keep it clean

When handling raw poultry always wash your hands and equipment thoroughly before going on to the next task to avoid possible cross contamination. Don't allow raw poultry to come into contact with other food, especially cooked food.

Making escalopes

To make chicken escalopes, simply split a chicken breast fillet in half horizontally with a knife, then place each half between two sheets of baking paper and pound with a rolling pin until flattened. Pan-fry with fresh herbs such as thyme, and deglaze the pan with white wine.

POULTRY

CHICKEN CACCIATORA

1.5 kg chicken, cut into 8 pieces
2 tablespoons olive oil
2 onions, sliced
2 x 425 g cans good-quality crushed tomatoes
2 cloves garlic, finely chopped
2 tablespoons tomato paste (purée)
1 teaspoon sugar
1 1/2 tablespoons finely chopped rosemary
2 bay leaves
3/4 cup (185 ml) dry white wine
1/2 cup (125 ml) chicken stock
1 tablespoon lemon juice
1/2 cup (80 g) kalamata olives (optional)

Cut any excess skin and fat from the chicken pieces, and season them well with salt and black pepper. Heat the oil in a heavy-based frying pan over medium–high heat and cook the chicken pieces a few at a time until golden brown. Remove from the pan.

Add the onion to the pan and cook over low heat until wilted and just starting to caramelise (this will take about 10 minutes). Don't let it brown too much. Add the tomato, garlic, tomato paste, sugar, herbs, wine and stock, bring to the boil, then reduce the heat and simmer, uncovered, for 15 minutes, or until reduced by about half.

Add the chicken pieces to the sauce and season well with salt and pepper. Add the lemon juice, cover and cook over very low heat for 30 minutes. Add the olives, then remove from the heat and leave, covered, for 10 minutes. Serve the cacciatora with buttered noodles or a green salad. Serves 4.

CREAMY CHICKEN WITH TARRAGON

1.5 kg chicken, cut into 8 pieces
2 1/2 tablespoons wholegrain mustard
1 teaspoon chopped tarragon, plus extra to garnish
45 g butter
2 teaspoons olive oil
85 g streaky bacon or mild pancetta, finely chopped
3 French shallots, finely chopped
2 cloves garlic, finely chopped
1 tablespoon plain flour
3/4 cup (185 ml) dry white wine
1 1/4 cups (315 ml) chicken stock
1/2 cup (125 ml) cream

Put the chicken in a glass or ceramic dish. Mix 1 1/2 tablespoons mustard with the chopped tarragon and rub all over the chicken. Cover and refrigerate overnight. Preheat the oven to 180°C (350°F/Gas 4).

Melt the butter and oil in a frying pan over medium–high heat and brown the chicken joints in two batches until the skin is golden. Transfer to a lidded ovenproof casserole.

Add the bacon, shallots and garlic to the pan and cook until the bacon just starts to brown. Stir in the flour and cook for 1 minute. Add the wine, stock and remaining mustard and cook for about 5 minutes, until the sauce is smooth. Pour over the chicken, then cover and bake for 1 hour 10 minutes.

Remove the chicken from the pan. Stir the cream into the sauce, then reduce the sauce over high heat until it reaches a coating consistency. Add the chicken to the sauce and stir until well coated. Serve the sauce over the chicken. Garnish with tarragon. Serves 4.

Poultry

CHICKEN TIPS

Lock in the moisture
To keep poultry moist when cooking, place softened butter (flavoured or plain) between the skin and the flesh. Before you do this, gently loosen the skin near the breast and thigh, making sure the skin stays intact. Another way is to cover the bird loosely with buttered foil — remove for the last 20–30 minutes of the cooking time to allow the skin to brown. A lemon wedge or half an onion placed in the cavity during cooking also adds moisture and flavour.

Browning adds flavour
Browning chicken pieces before stewing or casseroling adds flavour and colour to the final dish.

Quick roast
To roast a chicken quickly, cut it down the back and remove the backbone. Lay it flat on a baking tray, season under the skin with lemon and garlic butter, and roast till the juices run clear, basting frequently.

Save your bones
Save the bones from a carved roast chicken to use for stock; they can be frozen until you are ready to use them.

Chicken mince
For something different, try using chicken mince in place of beef mince in meatloaf, burgers, lasagne or bolognaise sauce.

Marinate in buttermilk
Marinate chicken in buttermilk overnight before rolling in seasoned flour and frying for a tender, moist flesh with a crisp skin.

Chargrilled spatchcock
Split spatchcocks (small chickens or poussin) in half and press down to flatten them out (this is called 'spatchcocking'). Marinate in thyme, garlic, olive oil and lime before cooking on the barbecue or chargrill.

Make the most of leftovers
Leftover cooked chicken or turkey makes a great base for salads, or can be shredded and added at the last minute to noodle soups such as laksa, or rice dishes like risotto or pilaf.

MEAT

MEAT

There are numerous cuts of beef, veal, lamb and pork, each with their own flavour and cooking qualities. It is important to select the best and most appropriate meat for your recipe.

CUTS AND COOKING METHODS

Tender cuts of meat have little connective tissue and therefore require less cooking time. These cuts are suitable for dry cooking methods such as grilling, barbecuing or frying. Tougher cuts need to be stewed or braised in moist heat with additional liquid over a longer cooking time, which breaks down the connective tissue and tenderises the meat. For this type of cooking, inexpensive cuts will still produce a succulent, delicious result. Cuts from the loin section of the hind quarter are the most tender.

Barbecuing

Beef: steaks (blade, fillet, minute steak, rib, rib eye, rump, sirloin (New York), Porterhouse, T-bone steak, mince, spareribs.

Veal: chops/cutlets/steaks (fillet, forequarter, loin, leg, rump, schnitzel, shoulder), eye of loin.

Lamb: chops/cutlets (chump, forequarter, leg, mid loin rib, rib loin, shoulder), eye of loin (backstraps), leg steak, fillet, mince, noisettes.

Pork: American-style ribs, boneless loin, butterfly steak, forequarter chops, spareribs, foreloin roast and steak, leg steak, loin chops, loin medallion steak.

Grilling

Beef: steaks (fillet, minute steak, oyster blade, rib, rib eye, rump, sirloin, T-bone), mince, spareribs.

Veal: chops/cutlets/steaks (fillet, forequarter, loin, leg, rump, schnitzel, shoulder), eye of loin.

Lamb: chops/cutlets (chump, forequarter, leg, mid loin, rib loin, shoulder), eye of loin (backstraps), fillet, leg steak, mince, noisettes.

Pork: American-style ribs, butterfly steaks, cutlets, diced pork, fillet, forequarter chops, leg schnitzels, leg steak, loin chops, loin medallion steak, spareribs.

Braising

Beef: bolar blade, brisket, chuck, round, shin, skirt.

Veal: shin (osso buco), shoulder, shanks.

Lamb: chump, forequarter, leg, shanks, shoulder.

Pork: forequarter chops, loin medallions, shanks, spareribs, trotters.

Pan-frying

Beef: steaks (fillet, minute, oyster blade, rib, rib eye, round, rump, sirloin, T-bone), mince, spareribs.

Veal: chops/cutlets/steaks (fillet, forequarter, loin, leg, rump, schnitzel, shoulder), eye of loin, mince.

Lamb: chops/cutlets (best neck, chump, forequarter, leg, mid loin, rib loin, shoulder), eye of loin (backstraps), fillet, leg steak, mince, noisettes.

Pork: butterfly steaks, forequarter chops, cutlets, fillet, diced pork, leg schnitzels, leg steak, loin chops, loin medallion steak, spareribs, mince.

Stir-frying

Beef: blade, fillet, rib eye, round, rump, sirloin.

Veal: eye of loin, fillets, leg, rump.

Lamb: eye of loin (backstraps), fillet, leg, shoulder.

Pork: thinly sliced leg or loin steaks, fillet, neck.

Roasting

Beef: blade, fillet, eye fillet, mince (as meatloaf), rib eye, rump, set of ribs, silverside, sirloin, topside.

Veal: fillet, leg, loin/eye of loin, rump, shoulder.

Lamb: chump, eye of loin (backstraps), forequarter, mid loin, mince, rack/crown roast, shanks, shoulder.

Pork: boneless loin, cutlets, fillet, foreloin roast, leg, forequarter, loin medallion, mince, neck, shoulder.

NOTE: Resting meats after roasting and before carving enhances the tenderness. This allows the muscles to relax and the juices to flow back from the exterior into the centre and baste the meat internally. To rest a roast, remove it from the pan, place on a warmed plate with a lip to catch any juices and cover with foil. Leave in a warm place for at least 10 minutes. Use this time to prepare the gravy, making the most of the delicious pan juices.

OSSO BUCO WITH GREMOLATA

2 tablespoons olive oil
1 onion, finely chopped
1 clove garlic, crushed
1 kg veal shin slices (osso buco)
2 tablespoons plain flour
410 g can tomatoes, roughly chopped
1 cup (250 ml) white wine
1 cup (250 ml) chicken stock

GREMOLATA
2 tablespoons finely chopped parsley
2 teaspoons grated lemon rind
1 teaspoon finely chopped garlic

Heat 1 tablespoon oil in a large shallow flameproof casserole dish. Add the onion and cook over low heat until soft and golden. Add the garlic, cook for 1 minute, then remove from the dish.

Heat the remaining oil over medium heat and brown the veal in batches, then remove. Return the onion to the casserole and stir in the flour. Cook for 30 seconds and remove from the heat. Slowly stir in the tomato, wine and stock, combining well with the flour. Return the veal to the casserole.

Bring to the boil over high heat, stirring, then reduce the heat to low so that the casserole is just simmering. Cook, covered, for 2¹/₂ hours, or until the meat is very tender and almost falling off the bones.

To make the gremolata, combine the parsley, lemon rind and garlic in a bowl. When the osso buco is ready, sprinkle the gremolata over the top and serve with risotto or plain rice. Serves 4.

MEAT TIPS

Per person
Allow 125–200 g lean boneless meat per person, or 250–300 g for cuts with a bone (eg T-bone steak).

Freeze in portions
When freezing meat it is sensible to freeze it in portions. Smaller cuts can be wrapped and frozen individually, so that if the number of serves required changes, you can defrost the exact amount you need and prevent wastage. Labels with the date of freezing, type of meat and number of serves can help you keep track of your freezer's contents.

Marinating meat
Marinating promotes both flavour and tenderness, as it was originally used to break down fibres and tenderise tougher cuts. Common marinade ingredients include wine, vinegar, lemon, yoghurt or chopped tomato, as the acid in these ingredients helps to break down connective tissue. Oil is also used to enhance the meat's juiciness. Marinating is great for barbecued and grilled meats. You can also stir-fry marinated meat, but make sure you drain it very well before cooking in a very hot wok, otherwise the meat will stew and become tough.

Pounding to tenderise
Scoring or pounding meat with a mallet or rolling pin also tenderises meat as it breaks down the connective tissue. Place plastic wrap between the meat and the mallet to prevent the meat from tearing. This method is commonly used when preparing schnitzel as it helps the meat to cook more quickly and evenly, so the interior is cooked through before the exterior burns.

Tender barbecued steak
When barbecuing steak, sear over the hottest part of the fire or heat first then move to a cooler area to cook through. It is recommended that steak only be turned once for maximum tenderness.

Slice meat thinly
To make it easier to slice meat thinly for stir-fries, place the meat in the freezer for half an hour before slicing as this makes it firmer. Do not do this with meat that has already been frozen and defrosted as this could lead to food poisoning.

MEAT

VEAL ESCALOPES WITH LEMON

4 large veal escalopes
plain flour, seasoned with salt and pepper
1 tablespoon olive oil
2 tablespoons butter
80 ml (¹/3 cup) dry white wine
250 ml (1 cup) chicken stock
60 ml (¹/4 cup) lemon juice
2 tablespoons capers, rinsed, and chopped if large
1 tablespoon finely chopped parsley
8 caperberries

Place the veal between two sheets of plastic wrap and pound with a meat mallet until an even thickness. Lightly dust each side with flour.

Heat the olive oil and butter in a large frying pan. Fry the escalopes over moderately high heat for about 2 minutes on each side, or until golden. Season and transfer to a warm plate.

Add the wine to the pan, increase the heat to high and boil until there are just 3–4 tablespoons of liquid left. Pour in the stock and boil for 4–5 minutes, or until it has reduced and slightly thickened. Add the lemon juice and capers and cook, stirring, for 1 minute. Taste for seasoning, then return the escalopes to the pan and heat through for 30 seconds. Sprinkle with parsley and serve at once, garnished with caperberries. Serves 4.

RACK OF LAMB WITH MUSTARD CRUST AND PARSLEY POTATOES

2 racks of lamb (6 chops per rack), trimmed
¹/4 cup (60 ml) oil
2 cups (160 g) fresh breadcrumbs
3 cloves garlic, chopped
1 teaspoon grated lemon rind
¹/2 cup (10 g) finely chopped parsley
2 tablespoons tarragon Dijon mustard
150 g unsalted butter, softened
400 g baby new potatoes

Preheat the oven to 220°C (425°F/Gas 7). Score the fat side of the racks in a criss-cross pattern. Rub with 1 tablespoon oil and season well. Heat the remaining oil in a frying pan over medium heat and cook the racks for 5–8 minutes, or until the surface is completely brown. Remove from the pan.

Combine the breadcrumbs, garlic, lemon rind and three-quarters of the parsley. Mix with the mustard and 100 g of the butter to form a paste. Firmly press a layer of breadcrumb mixture over the fat side of the racks, then place in a roasting tin. Bake for 25 minutes, or until the breadcrumbs are brown and crisp and the meat is cooked to medium. For well-done, continue to bake for 10 minutes, or until cooked to your liking. Cover the breadcrumb crust with foil to prevent it burning, if necessary.

About 25 minutes before the lamb is ready, toss the potatoes with the remaining butter until well coated. Season, then put in a roasting tin. Bake for 20 minutes, or until brown, then sprinkle with parsley and season. To serve, cut the racks in half using the bones as a guide. Serve with the pan juices. Serves 4.

MEAT TIPS

Rest and relaxation

In addition to roasted meats, which rest for at least 10 minutes, grilled, barbecued and pan-fried meat also benefit from resting for a few minutes before serving. This allows the fibres to relax and reabsorb their juices.

Roasting guide

As a general guide, roasted joints on the bone should be cooked in the oven at 240°C (475°F/Gas 9) for the first 15 minutes, after which the temperature should be reduced to 180°C (350°F/Gas 4) for the rest of the cooking time. A boneless roast can cook at 220°C (425°F/Gas 7) for the whole time. A joint on the bone will take 15 minutes per 500 g to roast to rare, 20 minutes to medium, and 25 minutes to well done. A boneless piece, on the other hand, will take 10 minutes per 500 g to roast to rare, 15 minutes to medium, and 20 minutes to well done.

Degreasing the pan

To degrease a pan before making gravy from the pan juices you can either use a gravy separator, use a spoon to skim visible oil from the surface or blot the surface with paper towels or bread. You could also try skimming the surface with ice cubes as this helps the oil to coagulate and makes it easier to remove with a spoon.

Dress up your leftovers

For a different way to serve leftover casseroles or stews, simply reheat and place them in a pie dish. Top with ready-made pastry and bake to make a quick and easy pie.

Mashed potato to the rescue

When cooking fatty cuts of pork, serve with mashed potato, chestnuts or legumes such as lentils, as they soak up some of the fat. Potatoes are added to braised or stewed pork dishes in Portugal and Spain half an hour before serving, as they absorb the fat which has risen to the top of the pan during cooking.

Handling cooked and raw meat

Never handle cooked and raw meat together as bacteria can be readily transferred between them by your hands and utensils.

QUICK RECIPE IDEAS

Pork cutlets with fennel and garlic

Oven roast pork cutlets with quartered bulbs of fennel and cloves of garlic, then serve on soft polenta with wedges of lemon and deep-fried sage leaves.

Spicy fajitas

Skirt steak is often overlooked. Try marinating it with chilli and lime, grill until cooked to your liking, slice and serve in fajitas with avocado and tomato salsa.

Beef fillet with a pepper crust

For a tasty variation on a pepper crust for beef fillet, use a combination of black peppercorns, Szechuan peppercorns and pink peppercorns roughly crushed in a mortar and pestle.

Roast lamb with garlic and rosemary

Make even slits in a leg of lamb and fill with slivers of garlic and sprigs of rosemary, rub all over with seeded mustard and sprinkle with sea salt and freshly ground pepper before roasting.

Warm Asian salad

Roast the narrower tail ends of beef fillet to rare, rest and slice thinly. Toss through a dressing of lime, fish sauce, chilli and a splash of rice vinegar for a delicious warm Asian salad.

Lamb with cinnamon and coriander

Slowly braise lamb shanks in stock with crushed tomatoes, a cinnamon stick and crushed coriander seeds. Serve on a bed of steamed couscous.

Calves liver with creamy mash

Fresh calves liver is delicious sliced thinly and cooked lightly and quickly on each side, so that it is still pink in the centre (overcooking will make the liver tough, dry and leathery). Serve with creamy mash and caramelised onions, drizzled with the pan juices.

Gourmet scotch fillet sandwich

Fill grilled sourdough with pan-seared scotch fillet, rocket, finely sliced Gruyère and tomato chutney.

Lamb loins with sumac

Coat lamb loins in sumac (a spice made from Middle Eastern berries), then pan-sear and allow to rest. Slice and serve with tabbouleh and a baby spinach salad.

SALADS & VEGETABLES

SALADS & VEGETABLES

These hints on buying and storing vegetables and salad greens will help you make the most of fresh vegetables in season.

Leafy green vegetables

Don't buy greens that are wilted, dry-looking or have yellow or brown patches. Crisp-head lettuces (such as iceberg and cos) should feel firm when squeezed and the base should be dry. To store, wrap them in vegetable bags, seal tightly and keep in the vegetable section of the fridge for 2–3 days.

Brassicas

Broccoli florets should be tightly closed and deep green with no sign of yellow. Cauliflower should have creamy florets firmly clustered together. Look for firm cabbages with unblemished outer leaves and a core that is not split or slimy. Choose similar-sized sprouts so they cook evenly. Keep in plastic bags in the vegetable compartment of the fridge for 3–5 days.

Legumes

Beans and peas should be bright green, crisp, have no wrinkles in their skin, and should snap rather than bend when broken. To choose sweet corn pull back the husks on the cobs to check that the kernels are fresh, plump, pale, even sized and show no signs of mould. Store in the fridge for 2–3 days.

Shoot and stalky vegetables

Choose asparagus with tightly bunched heads and ends that are dry and not withered or woody. Look for rounded, fat fennel bulbs that are white and firm. Fresh celery should be heavy, have thick, crisp ribs, a sound base and light green leaves. Look for globe artichokes with silky, tightly closed green heads and no dark patches. All the vegetables in this group deteriorate quickly and should be eaten as soon as possible after purchasing.

Roots and tubers

Carrots, turnips, parsnips, beetroot and all potatoes should be unblemished, feel hard to the touch and should not be sprouting or have a green tinge. Store in a cool, dry and dark place that is well ventilated. Storing potatoes in the refrigerator is not a good idea as this can make them develop a sweetish taste.

Eggplant (Aubergine)

Eggplants should be firm with a glossy, smooth skin and feel heavy for their size (this means they will have fewer bitter seeds). Eggplant will keep in the vegetable crisper in the fridge for up to a week.

Tomatoes and avocados

Choose the reddest tomatoes you can find (vine-ripened have the best flavour) and store them at room temperature away from direct sunlight. Ripe avocados are firm and supple — avoid those with bruised or spotted skins. To ripen a hard avocado, put it in a paper bag in a warm place for 2 days.

Capsicums (peppers) and chillies

Choose glossy, smooth, firm capsicums and chillies with no wrinkles or soft, brownish patches. Store in the refrigerator for up to a week, preferably not in plastic as they will sweat.

Cucumbers and squashes

Cucumbers should be crisp and firm, with no soft spots, and will keep in the fridge for up to a week. Pumpkins should be unblemished, with thick, firm, unbroken skin and no soft spots or splits. Keep for 3–4 months in a dry, ventilated place. Choose firm zucchini (courgette) and squash, with unblemished, glossy, smooth skins. Refrigerate in a bag for 2–3 days.

Bulb vegetables

Onions and garlic should have crackling papery skins and firm flesh. Reject any that are sprouting, mouldy, soft or wet. Store in a dry, airy place for a month. Choose spring onions (scallions) with fine green tops and white bulbs and use within a few days.

Mushrooms

Choose mushrooms which look firm, full and moist, with unblemished caps. Store in a paper bag in the fridge for 3–4 days. Avoid storing mushrooms in plastic as they will sweat and begin to decay.

CAESAR SALAD

3 eggs
2–3 cloves garlic, crushed
2–3 anchovies
1 teaspoon Worcestershire sauce
2 tablespoons lime juice
1 teaspoon Dijon mustard
3/4 cup (185 ml) light olive oil
3 slices white bread, crusts removed
20 g butter
2 tablespoons olive oil
3 rashers bacon
1 large or 4 baby cos lettuce
75 g shaved Parmesan
anchovies, extra, to garnish

Blend the eggs, garlic, anchovies, Worcestershire sauce, lime juice and mustard in a food processor until smooth. With the motor running, slowly add the olive oil in a thin stream to produce a creamy dressing. Season to taste.

Cut the bread into 1.5 cm cubes. Melt the butter and olive oil in a frying pan over medium heat, add the bread and cook until crisp. Remove from the pan. Cook the bacon rashers until crispy, then break them into even-sized pieces.

Combine the lettuce leaves with as much dressing as you want, then stir in the croutons, bacon and shaved Parmesan. Garnish with a couple of anchovies, if desired. Serves 4–6.

Note: Leftover dressing will keep in an airtight container in the fridge for 2–3 days. Lightly whisk before using if the mixture has separated.

SALADS &
VEGETABLES

VEGETABLE TIPS

Cooking with eggplant (aubergine)

Salting eggplant before cooking will draw out excess moisture, leaching away any bitterness, and will also reduce the amount of oil needed for cooking. Salting is not necessary for young, fresh eggplant.

Peeling tomatoes

Skin tomatoes by making a small cross in the base of the tomatoes, and plunging them into boiling water for 30 seconds, then straight into iced water. The skin should peel easily from the base.

Roasted garlic

For a milder and sweeter flavour, roast whole heads of garlic then squeeze out the softened cloves. Add to mashed potato, dressings or any other recipe where the garlic is not going to be cooked.

Remove the core from a lettuce

To remove the core from lettuce, hit the base of the lettuce hard on a bench to loosen the core, then turn it over and twist it out.

Globe artichokes

To prepare, twist off the long stems. Use a stainless steel knife to cut the base flat and rub the cut surface with lemon juice to prevent discolouration. Trim the tops off the long leaves, then wash and place in a bowl of acidulated water (water with lemon juice added). If you only require the artichoke hearts, pull off the large outer leaves by bending them over the base until they snap. When you get to the soft inner leaves, cut the cone of leaves away from the base. Trim away all the darker green parts from the sides and the base to form a neat round shape. Spoon out the inedible hairy choke and immerse the remainder in acidulated water or cook immediately according to your recipe.

Grilled capsicum (pepper)

Grill capsicums to blacken the skin, place in a plastic bag to cool, then peel away and discard the skin. This gives the capsicum flesh a wonderful smoky flavour.

Cooking whole onions

To prevent whole onions from disintegrating as they cook, simply peel then cut a cross-shaped incision into the root end.

SALADS & VEGETABLES

ASPARAGUS WITH HOLLANDAISE SAUCE

24 asparagus spears
2 egg yolks
2 teaspoons lemon juice
90 g unsalted butter, cut into cubes

Wash the asparagus and remove the woody ends (hold each spear at both ends and bend it gently—it will snap at its natural breaking point). Cook the asparagus in a frying pan of simmering salted water for 4 minutes, or until just tender. Drain, then cool under cold running water.

For the hollandaise sauce, put the egg yolks and lemon juice in a saucepan over very low heat. Whisk continuously, adding the butter piece by piece until the sauce thickens. Do not overheat or the eggs will scramble. Season.

(Alternatively, put the eggs yolks, salt and pepper in a blender and mix together. Heat the lemon juice and butter together until boiling and then, with the motor running, pour onto the yolks in a steady stream.)

Arrange a few asparagus spears on each plate and spoon the hollandaise over the top. Serves 4.

MIXED LEAF SALAD

DRESSING
1 clove garlic, cut in half
1/2 cup (125 ml) extra virgin olive oil
2 tablespoons white wine vinegar
2 teaspoons Dijon mustard
1/2 teaspoon sugar

50 g snow pea (mangetout) sprouts
150 g mixed lettuce leaves
80 g baby spinach leaves
50 g edible flower petals

For the dressing, skewer the garlic onto a toothpick and sit it in a jug with the combined oil, vinegar, mustard and sugar. Leave the garlic to infuse while preparing the salad.

Trim the ends from the snow pea sprouts. Rinse the lettuce and spinach leaves under running water and drain well. Toss with the snow pea sprouts and flowers in a large bowl, cover with plastic wrap and refrigerate until ready to serve.

To serve, remove and discard the garlic clove from the dressing, whisk until well blended and season with salt and freshly ground black pepper. Place the salad in a serving bowl and drizzle with the dressing. Serves 6–8.

SALADS & VEGETABLES

VEGETABLE TIPS

Fresh corn kernels

When corn kernels are required, it is easy to remove the fresh kernels from the cob. Remove the husk and silk, stand the cob upright or on an angle and, using a sharp knife, slice downwards between the cob and the kernels to separate them.

Peeling avocados

To easily peel ripe avocados, insert a knife until it just touches the stone and cut all the way around. Twist the two halves in opposite directions and gently pull apart. Embed the knife in the stone, twist and remove. Gently cut a slit down the skin of the avocado and pull the skin away in strips with your fingers.

Wilting spinach

As spinach and silverbeet reduce greatly in volume when cooked, you should allow 250 g per person. To wilt, simply place in an uncovered saucepan over low heat, using only the water that clings to the leaves after washing. Toss occasionally so it cooks evenly.

Juicy citrus fruit

To obtain the maximum amount of juice from citrus fruit (lemons, limes and oranges), roll them gently with the palm of your hand on the kitchen bench before squeezing. They can also be placed in the microwave on high for 20–30 seconds, as this softens the fruit.

Dicing onions

To quickly dice an onion, peel, trim one end flat, then place it on a chopping board. Make 5 or 6 slices through the onion, then turn it 90 degrees, hold the layers together firmly and cut across them. To minimise tears, peel under cold running water, then chop under a strong exhaust fan.

Mash with a twist

When boiling potatoes to mash, try adding some chopped parsnip, pumpkin or celeriac to the boiling water and mash with the potato. Delicious.

Vegetable juice

A quick way to make the most of vegetables is to extract the juice. Vegetable juices (alone or combined with fruit juice) make a vitamin-packed pick-me-up.

SALAD TIPS

Intense tomato flavour
Slowly roast tomato halves, then drizzle with olive oil and balsamic vinegar to intensify their flavour before adding to salads. Roma tomatoes are deliciously sweet when cooked this way.

Say it with flowers
For colour, flavour and texture consider adding some edible flowers to your salads. They are now readily available at most greengrocers.

Refresh salad greens
To refresh slightly wilted salad greens, plunge them briefly into a bowl of iced water, shake them dry and use quickly.

Seafood flavours
Add finely chopped anchovy, capers and dill to a dressing for a seafood salad.

Tenderise cabbage leaves
To tenderise tough leaves like cabbage for a salad, shred then steep them in boiling water for 10 minutes. Drain well, pressing down to remove excess moisture.

Red capsicums
When roasting whole red capsicums for a salad or antipasto platter, save the juice inside and add it to the dressing.

Marinated vegetables
Marinated and grilled vegetables stored in olive oil in a sterilised glass jar in the fridge are delicious salad stand-bys. Return to room temperature before using.

Time saver
Wash, spin and wrap your salad leaves in a tea towel, then place in a plastic bag and keep in the fridge until you are ready to serve.

Preparing potatoes for salads
Steam or simmer gently scrubbed, unpeeled whole potatoes, then drain thoroughly and slice into appropriate-sized pieces. Peel when cool enough to handle or leave with the skins on. Scrub the potatoes gently, then toss in the dressing while still warm. Slightly roughing up the surface enhances the potatoes' ability to absorb the dressing flavours.

DESSERTS

DESSERTS

Whether it's a creamy custard dessert or a refreshing fruit sorbet, dessert is the part of a home-cooked meal we all look forward to. Served with just the right accompaniment, you can't go wrong.

TYPES OF DESSERT

Egg-based desserts

Custards, ice creams, mousse and meringues are all egg-based. Custard can be baked in a water bath to make such favourites as crème brûlée and crème caramel. Crème pâtissèrie is a thickened custard used in fruit tarts or for filling profiteroles. Mousse and bavarois are thickened, moulded and chilled custards; and tiramisu, an Italian concoction, is a coffee-flavoured layered dessert with sponge fingers, custard and mascarpone.

Baked desserts

Baked desserts such as pastries, cakes, pies and tarts are familiar and favourite desserts, and can require a little more effort than other types of desserts but are certainly worth it. Soufflés, while not as difficult as their reputation might suggest, *do* need to be prepared carefully. Don't overwhip the egg whites, fold them gently into the soufflé base and bake immediately. Serve straight out of the oven.

Puddings

Puddings are often steamed for hours in a pudding basin to bring out the rich flavour and dense texture that they are noted for. Originally composed of fat such as suet, dried fruits, starch, spices and spirits, puddings are now made with a range of flavourings, such as chocolate, fruit, ginger and, of course, dates. They are often served with a sauce that enhances the base flavour, such as toffee, lemon or chocolate.

Fruit desserts

Whether fruit is eaten fresh, baked whole, used as a pie or pastry filling, puréed, poached or transformed into ice cream, gelato or sorbet, the finished product will depend greatly on the quality of its ingredients. Select firm, ripe fruit, avoiding any with bruised or discoloured skin, and take advantage of surplus fruits in season. Many stone fruits are delicious preserved in spiced liqueurs. Dried fruit poached with cinnamon, cloves and your favourite liqueur make a wonderful winter dessert when there is not always a great variety of fresh fruit available.

Chilled and frozen desserts

These include jellies, ice cream, gelato, granita and sorbet. These can be desserts in themselves, used as a base or filling for other frozen desserts or served as an accompaniment to a myriad of other sweets.

Fried desserts

While pan-frying and deep-frying are not generally associated with desserts, crepe and fritter batters form the base for many desserts. Crepes or pancakes can be wrapped around fillings, eaten simply with lemon juice and sugar, stacked and drenched with sauces, infused with flavourings or layered to form a 'cake'. Sweet fritters are deep-fried batter, sometimes containing fruit or nuts. Often dusted with sugar, they are best eaten hot, fresh from the pan.

ACCOMPANIMENTS

For a change from the expected accompaniments of cream or ice cream, the following ideas can be used to add flair to even the simplest desserts:

- Crème fraîche or French soured cream is delicious with fruit desserts.

- Mascarpone is a rich, heavy cream cheese served in Italy with pastries, cakes and fruit.

- Yoghurt makes an excellent foil for very sweet desserts, or sweeten thick Greek-style yoghurt with honey and serve simply with fresh fruits.

- Sorbet or gelato make a light and refreshing change to ice cream.

- Crème anglaise is a thin pouring custard that is perfect served with baked desserts and puddings.

- Fruit coulis (puréed fruit with sugar) should be light and not overly sweet, but with a pure taste of fruit. Try berry coulis with rich chocolate cake.

CREME BRULEE

6 egg yolks
1/2 cup (125 g) caster sugar
2 1/2 cups (625 ml) cream
1/2 vanilla bean, halved lengthways

Preheat the oven to 150°C (300°F/Gas 2). Whisk the egg yolks and 1/4 cup (60 g) caster sugar in a large heatproof bowl until thick and pale. Place the cream and vanilla bean in a saucepan, bring to the boil, then reduce the heat and simmer for 8 minutes. Remove from the heat and discard the vanilla bean. Slowly whisk the cream into the egg mixture, whisking continuously to prevent the eggs from scrambling. Strain the custard into a large jug, then pour immediately into six 100 ml ovenproof dishes.

Place the dishes in a baking dish. Pour sufficient hot water into the baking dish to come 2 cm below the top of the dishes and bake for 40 minutes, or until set. Remove and leave to cool, then cover and refrigerate overnight.

Sprinkle the remaining sugar evenly over the custards and refrigerate for 1 hour. Place the dishes in a shallow baking tray and pack ice cubes around them. Grill the custards under a very hot grill for 2–3 minutes, or until the sugar has melted and is lightly browned. Allow to set or harden before serving. Serves 6.

DESSERT TIPS

Bread and butter pudding
A simple twist on a classic dessert when making bread and butter pudding is to use brioche, panettone or croissant instead of sliced white bread.

Freeze cakes for trifle
Freeze any leftover butter or sponge cakes to use later in trifles.

Crème brûlée
For crème brûlée with a difference, try adding a liqueur to the mixture before baking or infuse the custard with scented spices like cardamom or star anise. Stir crushed pistachios, candied ginger or your favourite fruit through the mixture for added texture.

Candied fruit to garnish
Thinly sliced rounds of oranges, lemons, limes and blood oranges can be candied in sugar syrup and used as a spectacular garnish for desserts.

Smooth mousse
To help your chocolate mousse obtain an even texture, whip a small amount of the chocolate mixture into the beaten egg whites before adding the remaining chocolate.

Balsamic strawberries
For strawberries and cream with a twist, macerate fresh strawberries in balsamic vinegar and sugar, then serve with thick cream.

Vanilla sugar
When using vanilla beans in dessert recipes don't discard the scraped pod. Rinse well, allow to dry then add it to a jar of caster sugar. The flavour will infuse throughout the sugar.

Custard perfection
Stirred custard must be cooked very carefully and stirred frequently to prevent it boiling and curdling.

Cheese for dessert
A selection of good cheeses with fresh and dried fruit is a quick, easy dessert option. Include at least one soft cheese, one hard cheese, a blue cheese and an unusual cheese. Accompany with fresh grapes and figs, or dried apricots.

DESSERTS

CHOCOLATE MOUSSE

250 g dark chocolate, chopped
3 eggs
1/4 cup (60 g) caster sugar
2 teaspoons dark rum
1 cup (250 ml) cream, softly whipped

Put the chopped chocolate in a heatproof bowl. Half fill a saucepan with water and bring to the boil. Remove from the heat and place the bowl over the pan, making sure the base is not touching the water. Stir occasionally until the chocolate is melted, then set aside to cool.

Using an electric mixer, beat the eggs and sugar in a small bowl for 5 minutes, or until thick, pale and increased in volume.

Beat in the melted chocolate and the rum, then transfer the mixture to a large mixing bowl. Using a large metal spoon, gently fold in the cream until the mixture is just combined.

Spoon the mousse into four 1-cup (250 ml) dessert glasses. Refrigerate for 2 hours, or until set. Serves 4.

FRESH FRUIT SALAD WITH GINGER LIME SYRUP

1/2 small ripe pineapple, cut into 3.5 cm cubes
250 g strawberries, halved
500 g watermelon, cut into 3.5 cm cubes
300 g rockmelon, cut into 3.5 cm cubes
1/2 pawpaw, cut into 3.5 cm cubes
3 tablespoons small fresh mint leaves
1/4 cup (45 g) soft brown sugar
1/2 cup (125 ml) lime juice
2 cm x 2 cm piece fresh ginger, shredded

Put the fruit and mint in a large bowl and gently mix it all together.

Put the sugar, lime juice and 1/2 cup (125 ml) water in a small saucepan. Stir over low heat until the sugar has dissolved. Add the ginger and bring to the boil, then reduce the heat and simmer for 10 minutes, or until reduced. Cool slightly, then pour over the fruit salad and refrigerate until cold. Serves 4.

Desserts

DESSERT TIPS

Chocolate ice cream

When making chocolate ice cream, replace some of the sugar with honey for a mellow sweet flavour or add some espresso coffee for a mocha flavour.

Fresh berries

When fresh berries are in season, soak them in liqueur or dessert wine and serve with cream.

Crepes on call

Crepes freeze surprisingly well. Layer them with baking paper, cover with plastic wrap and freeze until needed. Thaw and warm through in a low oven or in the microwave. Serve with your favourite sauce, or with a squeeze of lemon and a dusting of icing sugar.

Quinces

Quinces are a fruit that need to be cooked thoroughly to be enjoyed. They become a deep rich pinky red colour when cooked and develop a perfumed aroma. They can be served simply with thick cream, or used in tarts or cakes.

Simple fruit tart

Add some lemon or lime juice to a custard filling for a simple citrus tart.

Moody meringues

Don't attempt to make meringue on a humid day because moisture in the air may cause the baked whites to weep and not set properly.

Scented panna cotta

When making a panna cotta, infuse the milk and cream with lemon grass and ginger as a sweet end to an Asian meal.

Stone fruits

When using stone fruits for desserts make sure they are perfectly ripe, as baking or poaching will not improve the flavour or texture of unripe fruit.

Choc tops

Melt white or dark chocolate and mix with a little cream. Make small scoops of ice cream or sorbet with a melon baller, dip them in the chocolate mixture and freeze. Serve a few in a martini glass for dessert or individually as petits fours in summer.

BAKING

BAKING

To bake with confidence, you need to have the right ingredients and equipment. Our troubleshooting tips will arm you with the skills to succeed brilliantly on your next baking adventure.

BEFORE YOU START

- Read through the recipe before you start, gathering (and sifting, where appropriate) the ingredients and necessary equipment.
- Make sure the ingredients are fresh and not past their use-by date, and that ingredients like butter and water are chilled if specified in the recipe.
- Be accurate in your measurements, using standard metric measuring cups and spoons, and levelling them off properly.
- Check that the oven rack is on the right shelf and prepare the baking trays or tins (grease, line with baking paper or lightly dust, as specified in the recipe).
- Preheat the oven. To make sure the temperature remains constant, don't open the oven door at all during the first two thirds of the cooking time.
- When making biscuits or pastry, the rolling surface is important. Cool surfaces, such as marble, are best. On hot days it's a good idea to place your rolling board in the refrigerator before you start to ensure it is extra cool.

PROBLEM SOLVING

What may have gone wrong and how to avoid it next time:

Pastry

- If your shortcrust pastry base shrinks too much, the pastry was probably overworked or not chilled before baking. Alternatively, the pie weights may have been pressed too firmly against the sides.
- If your shortcrust is tough, the pastry dough was probably overworked during mixing or rolling, or too much water was added to the dough.
- If puff pastry has risen unevenly when cooked, the edges were not trimmed with a sharp knife or the glaze has dripped down the sides, gluing the layers together.
- If the filling leaks from a filo parcel, there may be too much filling or not enough filo layers. The oven may have been too hot, or the filling too moist.
- If choux pastry is poorly risen and dense inside, too little egg was added, or possibly the oven door was opened too soon during baking.

Cakes

- If the surface is cracked or peaked, the oven was too hot or the batter was overmixed.

- If the texture of the cake is coarse and the centre has sunk, either the oven was not hot enough, the batter was undermixed or too much baking powder has been added.

- If the cake doesn't rise as much as it should, and has a very compact texture, then either the baking powder is too old or not enough was used, or the butter or the eggs were too cold.

- If the cake is dry with a tough crust then the cake has been overbaked or the tin was too large.

- If the cake is burnt on the top or bottom, but the batter is undercooked, the problem lies with uneven heat or air circulation in the oven.

Bread

- If your yeast mixture has not risen and is not frothy, the yeast is dead. If this happens, you will have to throw it away and start again. And make sure the water is tepid — if it is too warm it may kill the yeast.

- If there are large holes in the loaf and it has risen too much, the dough may have been insufficiently kneaded during the first kneading stage. The rising time may have been too long, or the dough may not have been correctly knocked back before shaping the loaf.

- If the bread has an uneven colour, the oven temperature was uneven or too high, or the bread was placed too low in the oven. A hard crust forms if the dough is not covered during the rising stage, allowing the surface to dry out and thus form a crust.

APPLE PIE

6 large Granny Smith apples, peeled and sliced
2 tablespoons caster sugar
1 teaspoon finely grated lemon rind
pinch of ground cloves
2 cups (250 g) plain flour
3 tablespoons self-raising flour
150 g cold butter, chopped
2 tablespoons caster sugar
5 tablespoons iced water
2 tablespoons apricot jam
1 egg, lightly beaten
1 tablespoon sugar

Put the apple in a heavy-based saucepan with the sugar, rind, cloves and 2 tablespoons water. Cook gently until the apples are just tender. Drain and cool.

Sift the flours into a bowl and add the butter. Rub the butter into the flour with your fingertips until it resembles fine breadcrumbs. Mix in the sugar and make a well in the centre. Add the water and mix with a flat-bladed knife until the mixture comes together in beads. Gather the pastry together on a floured surface and divide into two, making one half a little bigger. Cover and refrigerate for 20 minutes.

Preheat the oven to 200°C (400°F/ Gas 6). Roll out the larger piece of pastry between two sheets of baking paper to line the base and side of a 23 cm pie plate. Peel off the top piece of baking paper and invert the pastry into the dish. Peel off the other baking sheet and trim off the excess pastry. Brush the jam over the base and spoon the apple filling into the shell. Roll out the remaining piece of pastry until large enough to cover the pie. Brush a little water around the rim, then place the top on, inverting the pastry off the baking paper. Trim off the excess pastry, pinch the edges together and cut a couple of steam slits in the top.

Brush the top lightly with egg, then lightly sprinkle with the sugar. Place on a preheated oven tray and bake for 20 minutes, reduce the temperature to 180°C (350°F/Gas 4) and bake for 20 minutes more, or until golden. Serves 6.

ΤΣΟΥΡΕΚΙ (Θεια Νικη)

15 eggs — 4kg Plain Flour
500g butter — 1½ kg sugar (castor)
3 cups milk — 3 cups O.J juice
O.J zest — Vanilla sugar
(1 tsp) Allspice — coriander seeds
Caraway — aniseed
2 pkts Mastiha — 2 pkts Mahlepi
2 tsp Baking Powder
400g yeast or 8 tbls dry yeast

METHOD

(In a bowl put warm milk
1 cup warm water, flour & leave
overnight.)
Beat eggwhites seperatly &
beat yolks ē sugar till white.
Mix all ingredients together
to a soft dough & let it
rise. Punch down & knead
again. Place on trays &
let it rise. (cook in gentle
oven app. 20-30 mins each).

ΚΟΥΛΟΥΡΑΚΙΑ (Θεια Νικη)

12 eggs (sep whites)
2 pkt butter
4 cups sugar
½ " oil
½ " Cream
1 tsp Ammonia
Vanilla extract
S.R.Flour (app 2kg)
O.J. Zest

ΚΟΥΛΟΥΡΑΚΙΑ (ΚΑΝΕΛΛΑΣ)

1 cup oil plus ¼ pkt butter
1 cup O.J & zest
1¾ " Castor sugar
Cinnamon
Cloves
S.R.Flour as needed.
Mix all ingredients together & add
flour as needed. Roll into sesame
seeds & bake

ARTICHOKE & (CRACKED) WHEAT BREAD

9oz Marinated Artichoke hearts

1/2 tbls Yeast

1 1/2 cups Bread Flour

1 1/2 " Wholemeal Flour

1/3 cup cracked wheat

1 1/2 tbls sugar

1/2 " Salt

1/4 tsp pepper

3 tbls Parmesan (grated)

1 cup warm water

Drain artichokes & chop. Put all ingredients & Select white Bread & Push start.

BAKING TIPS

How do you like your scones?
For soft scones, wrap them in a clean tea towel while still hot. If you prefer scones with a crisp top, transfer them to a wire rack to cool slightly before wrapping.

Pie overflow
Place your pie on a baking tray in the oven in case of any overflow during baking.

Lattice pastry
Use a lattice pastry topping for pies filled with juicy fruits such as berries. The contrasting colours look attractive, while the lattice effect allows steam to escape and the fruit juice to evaporate and caramelise. Roll out the pastry, cut into thin strips, then arrange half the strips on a sheet of baking paper. Interweave the remaining strips to form a lattice pattern, then place on the pie.

Buttermilk muffins
Using buttermilk instead of milk in a muffin mixture adds a lovely flavour, a soft texture and a crisp crust.

Flavoured meringues
Prepare a basic meringue mixture then flavour with cocoa powder, chocolate chips, instant coffee, custard powder or ground nuts.

Patch holes in pastry
To patch up holes in rolled flaky pastry, cut a piece from the edge, place it over the crack and dust it lightly with flour. Roll it into the dough until the hole is covered. It's a good idea to transfer the dough to the pie dish with the patched side on the bottom.

Lifting pastry into the pie dish
Roll out the pastry between two sheets of baking paper and remove the top sheet. Carefully invert the pastry over the pie dish (make sure you centre the pastry, as it can't be moved once in place), then peel away the paper.

Savoury pie crusts
A suet crust will produce a tender and flavoursome crust for a steak and kidney pie, or add Parmesan to the pastry for a vegetable tart. Simply using lard will produce the most tender, crisp and flaky crust of all.

BAKING

LEMON CAKE WITH CRUNCHY TOPPING

250 g unsalted butter, softened
3/4 cup (185 g) caster sugar
2 teaspoons finely grated lemon rind
4 eggs, lightly beaten
2 cups (250 g) self-raising flour
1 teaspoon baking powder
2 tablespoons lemon juice

TOPPING
1/2 cup (125 g) sugar
1/4 cup (60 ml) lemon juice

Preheat the oven to 170°C (325°F/Gas 3). Lightly grease a 22 cm square tin and line the base with baking paper.

Cream the butter and sugar in a small bowl with electric beaters until the mixture is light and fluffy. Beat in the lemon rind, then add the egg gradually, beating thoroughly after each addition. Transfer the mixture to a large bowl. Using a large metal spoon, fold in the combined sifted flour, baking powder and 1/4 teaspoon salt, as well as the lemon juice. Stir until the mixture is just combined and almost smooth.

Spoon the mixture into the tin and smooth the surface. Bake for 1 hour 20 minutes, or until a skewer comes out clean when inserted into the centre of the cake. Remove from the tin and turn out onto a wire rack.

For the topping, mix together the sugar and lemon juice (don't dissolve the sugar), and quickly brush over the top of the warm cake. The juice will sink into the cake, and the sugar will form a crunchy topping. Leave to cool. Makes 1.

APPLE CINNAMON MUFFINS

400 g can pie apple
2 1/2 cups (310 g) self-raising flour
2 teaspoons ground cinnamon
2/3 cup (125 g) soft brown sugar
1 1/3 cups (350 ml) milk
2 eggs
1 teaspoon vanilla essence
150 g unsalted butter, melted and cooled
1/2 cup (60 g) walnuts, finely chopped

Preheat the oven to 200°C (400°F/Gas 6). Lightly grease twelve regular muffin holes. Place the pie apple in a bowl and break up with a knife.

Sift the flour and cinnamon into a bowl and add the sugar. Make a well in the centre. Whisk together the milk, eggs and vanilla in a jug and pour into the well. Add the melted butter. Gently fold the mixture with a metal spoon until just combined. Add the pie apple and gently stir through. Don't overmix—the batter should be lumpy. Overmixing will make the cooked muffins tough.

Fill each muffin hole with the mixture (the holes will be quite full, but don't worry because these muffins don't rise as much as some) and sprinkle with walnuts. Bake for 20–25 minutes, or until the muffins are risen, golden and come away slightly from the tin. Cool for a couple of minutes, then gently loosen each muffin with a flat-bladed knife and transfer to a wire rack. Serve warm or at room temperature. Makes 12.

NOTE: Completely cool the melted butter before adding it. It doesn't always combine well with other liquids so it is often added separately.

CAMPAGNE !!

CBAKING

BAKING TIPS

Prevent biscuits burning
To help prevent biscuits from burning on the bottom during baking, double-pan or stack two baking trays together.

Whipping egg whites
Egg whites for meringue will whip to their maximum volume if they are at room temperature, and the beaters and bowl are dry and clean.

Spice up a lemon tart
Add a teaspoon of fresh grated ginger or lemon zest to the pastry when making a lemon tart.

Sweet and savoury scones
You can make both sweet and savoury additions to scone mixtures. Try adding sugar and spices, raisins, chopped dates or figs for sweet scones, and cheese, pumpkin, herbs or bacon for savoury scones.

Bread glazes
To obtain a deep crust colour on home-baked bread, glaze it before baking with a whole egg beaten with 1 teaspoon of water (or use just the egg yolk for a deeper colour). A whisked egg white glaze will offer a crisp crust, while a light crust can be formed by brushing the dough with milk or melted butter.

Did you know ... ?
Good-quality puff pastry has been turned an average of 6 times, has 729 layers and rises to approximately 8 times its original height.

Keep it cool
To maintain a cool temperature when making pastry in a food processor, place the food processor bowl and blade in the refrigerator before using.

Shape your muffins
To get nicely domed muffins that don't have 'ledges' on the sides, grease the muffin cups on the bottom and only halfway up the sides. Sprinkle the tops of muffins with demerara sugar before baking to give them a crunchy sweet top.

Cut pies easily
Pies will cut more easily if they are left to cool a bit and the filling is allowed to settle.

DECORATING CAKES

Spreading icing
Spread the icing or filling (except whipped cream) evenly with a long metal spatula that has been dipped in hot water. Clean the spatula between applications.

Icing sugar and fresh berries
A simple cake warm from the oven often needs nothing more than a dusting of icing sugar and some fresh berries to serve.

Chocolate, chocolate and more chocolate!
Chocolate is a versatile decorating tool — it may be curled, shaved, cut into shapes, or piped into a design then used to decorate the sides or top of the cake. Use a vegetable peeler to shave chocolate (this will be easier if the chocolate is at room temperature). Pile chocolate truffles on top of an iced chocolate cake for a luxurious and indulgent decoration.

Toasted nuts
If you are decorating a cake with nuts or coconut, toast them first. This will give a much better flavour.

Rose petals
Rose petals (which have not been sprayed) make beautiful cake decorations. Choose blemish-free petals, brush with whisked egg white, and dip into caster sugar. Gently shake off any excess sugar and leave on a tray to dry before decorating. Non-toxic leaves can be prepared in the same way.

Dust a design
Cut a stencil out of paper and lay it over your cake then dust with icing sugar or cocoa to create a simple patterned design on the surface of the cake.

Gold leaf
Use pieces of edible gold leaf for a decadent finish on a special cake.

Meringues
Decorate cakes with small meringues or skinny baton-shaped meringues, which will easily stick to the icing and may be coloured to suit the cake.

Serve on the side
Serve a very sweet cake with crème fraîche or mascarpone as a change from ice cream or cream.

JAMS
& PRESERVES

JAMS & PRESERVES

Making jams and preserves is a great way of taking advantage of fruit and vegetables while they are at their seasonal best. And the whole process is much simpler than you might think.

DEFINITIONS

- **Jam:** made from small pieces of fruit and sugar, cooked to a thick, spreadable consistency.
- **Preserve:** whole fruits preserved in a heavy sugar-based syrup.
- **Conserve:** whole or large pieces of fruit cooked with sugar until thick.
- **Jelly:** made from the strained juice of cooked fruits and sugar. Can contain small pieces of the fruit.
- **Marmalade:** sliced, cooked citrus fruits, suspended in a sweet, thick jam mixture.
- **Fruit curd:** thick, spreadable, creamy mixture made with juice, fruit purée, and sometimes citrus rind, combined with sugar, eggs and butter and cooked until thick.
- **Pickle:** vegetables, or sometimes fruit, pickled in vinegar with sugar, salt and spices.
- **Chutney:** mixture of vegetables and/or fruit, cooked with vinegar, sugar and spices to a thick pulpy consistency.
- **Relish:** salted cooked vegetables in a thick sugar, spice and vinegar-based sauce.

HOW IT ALL WORKS

While specific recipes have their own instructions, the general method for making jams and preserves is to first bring the mixture to the boil, then reduce the heat and simmer for the specified time until the fruit is tender. At this point, the warmed sugar is added. Remove any scum that comes to the surface during the cooking process, which is caused by impurities in the sugar or dirt on the fruit. Stir over the heat without boiling, until all the sugar has dissolved.

To dissolve any excess sugar crystals which can cause jam to crystallise towards the end of cooking, brush the side of the pan with a wet pastry brush. If the jam does crystallise, add 1–2 tablespoons of lemon juice and gently reheat (this may slightly alter the taste). Once all the sugar has dissolved, boil the mixture rapidly for the specified time. Stir frequently to speed up the cooking process and stop any jam sticking to the pan. When the cooking time is up, the mixture should fall from a wooden spoon heavily with 3 or 4 drops joining together as they drop. This means the jam or preserve has reached setting point.

SETTING POINT

Cooking times vary greatly between recipes depending on pan sizes, types of fruit and whether the fruit is in season. Therefore it is necessary to test for what is called the 'setting point', that is, when the jam has reached the stage where it will set to a desirable consistency. To test for setting point, place one teaspoon of the jam on a cold plate and place it in the freezer for 30 seconds or until the jam has cooled to room temperature. Gently push through the jam with your finger — there should be a skin on the top which should be wrinkled if the jam is ready. If not, return the jam to the heat and cook until it wrinkles when tested.

BOTTLING JAMS

As soon as setting point for jams is reached, the mixture should be transferred to warm, clean jars. If you leave it in the saucepan for too long, it will start to set and you will have to reheat it and repeat the setting point process. Jams with large pieces of fruit need to stand for a few minutes before bottling so the fruit is evenly suspended throughout the jam. Preserves are ready when they are placed on a saucer and leave a clean trail with no signs of runny liquid.

When bottling jams and preserves, remember that the mixture is extremely hot. Hold the jar with a tea towel and spoon or pour the mixture in, filling right to the top. Use a jam funnel if your jars have narrow tops, otherwise you can pour the mixture into a heatproof jug, then transfer it to the jars. Seal the jars while the mixture is still hot. Turn the jars upside down for 2 minutes, then invert and cool. This will ensure that the fruit is evenly distributed and the lids are sterilised.

STRAWBERRY CONSERVE

5 cups (1.25 kg) sugar
1.5 kg strawberries
1/2 cup (125 ml) lemon juice

Preheat the oven to 150°C (300°F/Gas 2). Spread the sugar in an even layer in a deep-sided baking dish and warm in the oven for 10–15 minutes, or until warmed through. Stir the sugar once or twice during warming to prevent it from clumping together. Put two small plates in the freezer.

Wipe the strawberries clean and hull them. Place them in a large saucepan with the lemon juice, warmed sugar and 1/2 cup (125 ml) water. Warm gently, without boiling, stirring carefully with a wooden spoon. Try not to break up the strawberries too much.

Increase the heat and, without boiling, continue to stir the mixture for 10 minutes, or until all the sugar has dissolved. Increase the heat and boil for 20 minutes, stirring often. Skim any scum off the surface with a skimmer or slotted spoon. Start testing for setting point after 20 minutes, but it may take up to 40 minutes. Be careful that the conserve does not catch on the base of the pan and start to burn.

Remove the pan from the heat, spoon a little conserve onto one of the cold plates and place in the freezer for 30 seconds. When setting point is reached, a skin will form on the surface and the jam will wrinkle when pushed with your finger. Remove any scum from the surface.

Spoon immediately into clean, warm jars and seal. Turn the jars upside down for 2 minutes, then invert and leave to cool. Label and date. Store in a cool, dark place for 6–12 months. Refrigerate after opening for up to 6 weeks. Makes 1.5 litres.

JAMS & PRESERVES TIPS

Keep jellies clear
To avoid cloudiness in jellies, take care not to squeeze or disturb the jelly bag while the fruit is dripping through.

Crystallisation
Crystallisation is usually caused by the addition of too much sugar, which was then not dissolved properly before boiling.

Fermentation
Fermentation can be the result of using mushy, overripe or damaged fruit during the cooking process or not adding enough sugar. If you reduce the amount of sugar in a recipe, make sure that you eat it within a few months as it won't keep for long. Refrigerate it after opening as the set will not be very strong.

Floating fruit
Floating fruit means that the mixture was not cooked sufficiently or did not stand for long enough before being boiled.

Mould
Mould starts to grow once the jar is opened if storing in a warm place, or if the mixture was not covered when it was hot.

Runny jam
Jam that is too runny has not set properly. Return it to the pan, bring it to the boil again and retest for the setting point before bottling.

Tough fruit
Tough fruit was not cooked for long enough before adding the sugar. Fruit will not soften further after the sugar is added.

Air bubbles
Occasionally the mixture in the jars will have air bubbles. To remove, simply use a clean, thin skewer to help push the mixture aside and release the bubble to the surface.

Don't cook too much at once
Try not to cook too much jam in one quantity. As a rough guide do not use more than 2 kg fruit in a recipe at one time.

JAMS & PRESERVES

TOMATO AND CHILLI RELISH

1 kg tomatoes
3 cooking apples (500 g), peeled, cored and grated
2 onions, chopped
1 teaspoon grated fresh ginger
4 cloves garlic, chopped
1–2 long red chillies, sliced
1 cup (230 g) soft brown sugar
1 cup (250 ml) cider vinegar

Cut a cross at the base of each tomato, place in a large bowl, cover with boiling water and leave for 30 seconds, or until the skins start to spilt. Transfer to a bowl of cold water. Peel away the skin, roughly chop the tomatoes and place in a large pan.

Add the remaining ingredients to the pan and stir over low heat until all the sugar has dissolved. Bring to the boil, then reduce the heat and simmer, stirring often, for 2–2^{1}/4 hours, or until the relish has reduced and thickened.

Spoon immediately into clean, warm jars, and seal. Turn the jars upside down for 2 minutes, then invert and leave to cool. Label and date. Leave for 1 month before opening to allow the flavours to develop. Store in a cool, dark place for up to 12 months. Refrigerate after opening, for up to 6 weeks. Good for serving with cooked or cold meats, or at a barbecue. Makes 1 litre.

FIG PRESERVE

4 cups (1 kg) sugar
1 kg fresh figs, stalks removed
^{1}/2 cup (125 ml) lemon juice

Preheat the oven to 150°C (300°F/Gas 2) for about 10 minutes. Put the sugar in a deep-sided baking dish and heat in the oven until warmed through, stirring a couple of times.

Put two small plates in the freezer. Put the figs in a large heatproof bowl. Cover with boiling water for 3 minutes. Drain, cool and cut into pieces. Put the figs, lemon juice and ^{1}/2 cup (125 ml) water in a large pan. Bring to the boil, then reduce the heat and simmer, covered, for 20 minutes, or until the figs are soft.

Add the sugar and stir over medium heat, without boiling, for 5 minutes, or until all the sugar has dissolved. Bring to the boil and boil for 20 minutes, stirring often. Remove any scum from the surface during cooking with a skimmer or slotted spoon. Add a little water if the mixture thickens too much. When thick and pulpy, start testing for setting point.

Remove from the heat, place a little preserve onto one of the cold plates and put in the freezer for 30 seconds. When setting point is reached, a skin will form on the surface and the preserve will wrinkle when pushed with your finger. Remove any scum from the surface.

Pour immediately into clean, warm jars, and seal. Turn the jars upside down for 2 minutes, then invert and leave to cool. Label and date. Store in a cool, dark place for 6–12 months. Refrigerate after opening for up to 6 weeks. Makes 1 litre.

JAMS &
PRESERVES

JAMS & PRESERVES TIPS

Sterilising jars
To sterilise a jar, wash both the jar and lid in hot soapy water and dry in a warm oven. Do not use a tea towel or the jar will no longer be sterilised.

Liqueur fruits
Fruits preserved in liqueur make a tasty and simple dessert; serve with mascarpone or vanilla ice cream.

Pickled onions
When pickling onions, blanch them whole in boiling water for 1 minute — the skins will then slip straight off. They are excellent with cheese and crusty bread, forming part of the traditional ploughman's lunch.

Marmalade
Seville oranges make wonderful marmalade due to their tart flesh and thick rough skin.

Strawberry flavour
Don't wash strawberries once they have been hulled as they will absorb the water, which will dilute the flavour.

Fruit curds
For a change from lemon or passionfruit curd, try making mango and lime, strawberry, dried apricot or cherry flavoured curd. For best results, make it with unsalted butter.

Jam glaze
For a shiny glaze and beautiful finish on fruit tarts melt a little jam or jelly with water and brush it over the surface of the fruit.

Home-made gifts
Home-made jams, preserves, liqueur fruits and curds make fantastic and special gifts.

Mango chutney
Green mango chutney is a traditional accompaniment to Indian-style dishes.

Spice flavour
When flavouring pickles and chutneys with dried spices like coriander, cumin or mustard seeds, crush them in a mortar and pestle, or with the flat side of a heavy knife first to release their aroma. This will give a much better flavour than purchased ground spices.

Published by Murdoch Books®, a division of Murdoch Magazines Pty Limited. First published 2003.
Murdoch Books® Australia, GPO Box 1203 Sydney NSW 2001
Phone: 61 (0) 2 4352 7000 Fax: 61 (0) 2 4352 7026
Murdoch Books® UK Limited, Ferry House, 51–57 Lacy Road, Putney, London SW15 1PR
Phone: + 44 (0) 20 8355 1480 Fax: + 44 (0) 20 8355 1499

Editorial Director:	Diana Hill
Creative Director:	Marylouise Brammer
Original Concept and Design:	Vivien Valk
Designer:	Tracy Loughlin
Production:	Fiona Byrne
Food Director:	Jane Lawson
Home Economist:	Valli Little
Photographer:	Craig Cranko
Stylist:	Mary Harris
Food Preparation:	Valli Little

All recipes developed in the Murdoch Books Test Kitchen

Chief Executive:	Juliet Rogers
Publisher:	Kay Scarlett

Produced by Phoenix Offset. PRINTED IN CHINA.

RECIPE CLIPPINGS